D0919192

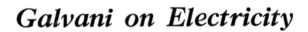

Galvani on Electricity

A TRANSLATION

of Luigi Galvani's *De Viribus Electricitatis*

Elizabeth Licht, Publisher   1953

30 Hillside Avenue, Cambridge, Massachusetts

In Motu Musculari Commentarius

Commentary on the

EFFECT OF ELECTRICITY
ON MUSCULAR MOTION

by Robert Montraville Green, M.D.

Emeritus Professor of Anatomy, Harvard Medical School,
Boston, Massachusetts

343243

UNIVERSITY
OF NEW BRUNSWICK

NOV 1 1985

LIBRARIES

Copyright 1953 by
Elizabeth Licht

All Rights Reserved

THE TEXT OF THIS PUBLICATION OR ANY PART
THEREOF MAY NOT BE REPRODUCED IN ANY MANNER
WHATSOEVER WITHOUT PERMISSION IN WRITING
FROM THE PUBLISHER

Harriet Irving Library
JUL 29 1971
University of New Brunswick

WAVERLY PRESS, INC.
BALTIMORE, MARYLAND

PRINTED IN THE UNITED STATES OF AMERICA

Preface

The name of Galvani has found its way into many languages as a common word because of a report he wrote on electricity in 1791 in Latin. That remarkable and important work has been translated into three languages but has never before been published in English. Most important documents on science were written in Latin up to the time of the eighteenth century. Until then most scientists could speak and write the language which was international and the mark of education. Galvani's commentary on electricity first appeared in a scientific journal, the seventh volume of the proceedings of the Bologna Academy and Institute of Sciences and Arts, in an issue dated March 27, 1791 (*De Bononiensi Scientiarum Et Artium Instituto Atque Academia Commentarii, 1791, VII, 363–418*). In the following year, Galvani's nephew, Giovanni Aldini, reprinted it in book form along with an introduction to electricity by himself in Latin, and two letters between Galvani and Carminati in Italian. Aldini also wrote a dozen footnotes to the original Galvani article. In order to illustrate his own footnotes, Aldini altered the four original illustrative plates of Galvani which had 17 figures, with three plates containing 27 figures. In this, the first complete English translation of Galvani, we have used the original four plates and therefor omitted the footnotes of Aldini which do nothing to improve the eloquently simple Galvani original. We have however included translations of the rest of the Aldini book published in Modena in 1792.

We believed that Galvani's contribution to electricity and electrophysiology was of such importance that it should become more available and available in English. We asked Doctor Robert M. Green, a scholar and linguist, to translate the original article and the rest of the Aldini book. To introduce this superior translation we invited the academic heir of Galvani, Dr. Giulio C. Pupilli, professor of physiology at the medical school of the University of Bologna, to recount the highlights of the life and writings of Galvani.

Additional thanks go to many who loaned encouragement and assistance: to the Rector of the University of Bologna, Dr. Sebastiano Mazzanachio, and to Dr. Biffi, Executive Secretary of the University of Bologna, for the Latin text and an Italian translation;

to the *Accademia dell'Istituto delle Scienze di Bologna,* for the privilege of inspecting the original manuscripts; to Dr. H. Fischgold of Paris for a copy of the French translation of Paul Antonin; to the Yale University Library for photographs of the illustrations; to the *Bibliothèque Nationale* of Paris for a copy of the German translation; and to the Boston Medical Library for the use of the Aldini edition.

SIDNEY LICHT, M.D.

Cambridge, Massachusetts.

Table of Contents

Introduction

The Bologna Institute of Arts and Sciences was founded by Count Luigi Ferdinando Marsili in 1714 in the Poggi Palace, the present seat of the University of Bologna. In 1785 the Institute began an annual publication (Commentaries) in the seventh volume of which appeared the report which is translated in full for the first time in the English language in this volume. *De viribus electricitatis in motu musculari Commentarius* (Commentary on the forces of electricity in their relation to muscular motion) was published in *De Bononiensi Scientiarum et Artium Instituto atque Academia Commentarii*, 1791, VII, 363–418. The author of this pioneering work in electrophysiology was the 54 year old Professor of Obstetrics at the Institute.[1] On the one-hundredth anniversary of his birth, the Academy of Sciences of the Institute published under one cover all the then known writings of Galvani[2] in addition to a *Rapporto* concerning them by the physicist Silvestro Gherardi. On the two-hundredth anniversary of his birth all other writings of Galvani discovered during the preceding century were published.[3] The importance of *De viribus* was appreciated in many countries very soon after publication and a half century later, the noted German physiologist du Bois-Reymond wrote, "The storm which began with the publication of this Commentary in the world of physics, physiology and

[1] In Galvani's time, at Bologna, the University and the Institute of Sciences were separate institutions. The University was located in the *Archiginnasio* in Peace Square, now called *Piazza Galvani*. The Institute was a sort of a graduate school of sciences and represented the active core of scientific life in Bologna, well known even abroad (Simeoni, L., *Storia dell'Universita di Bologna*. Vol. II, Bologna, 1947.) The Academy of *Inquieti* was founded sometime near 1690, thanks to the efforts of men interested in encouraging experimental trends in scientific research. The Academy merged with the Institute and took its name. Later on it was also called *benedettina*, in honor of Pope Benedict XIV of Bologna, who had been a great benefactor.

[2] Galvani, L. *Opere edite ed inedite*. Bologna, 1841. This volume includes: a) the *Rapporto sui manoscritti del celebre Professore Luigi Galvani*, by Professor Silvestro Gherardi. It was read before the Academy during the sessions of November 7 and 14, 1839; b) the *Elogio del celebre Professore Luigi Galvani*, by Professor Giuseppe Venturoli, read before the Academy on May 24, 1802.

[3] Galvani, L. *Memorie ed esperimenti inediti*. Bologna, 1937. This volume includes: a) a first Italian edition of *De viribus electricitatis*, with the Latin text (by E. Benassi); b) an essay on Galvani's iconography (by G. Zucchini); c) a description of Luigi Galvani's manuscripts in possession of the Royal Academy of Sciences of the Institute of Bologna (by L. Barbieri); d) a contribution to the bibliography of Galvani's published works (by L. Barbieri).

medicine, can only be compared to that which arose on Europe's political horizon during the same period in the final years of the eighteenth century."[4]

A year later, a second edition was published at Modena[5] in book form, and included a dissertation and notes by Giovanni Aldini (Galvani's nephew) together with letters from the correspondence between Galvani and Bassano Carminati, Professor of Medicine at the University of Pavia.[6] That book was responsible for a dispute between the schools of Bologna and Pavia. It is that book which is here presented for the first time in any language other than the original Latin.

Fulton and Cushing[7] have published a comprehensive bibliography *De viribus electricitatis* which lists a German translation published in 1793 at Prague by Johann Mayer[8] and another German version about a century later by Arthur Joachim von Oettingen at Leipzig.[9] The most recent publication and first French translation is that of Paul Antonin.[10]

Galvani first began his studies on animal electricity in 1780[11] but prudence and thoroughness delayed his decision to publish his findings. He was performing experiments on nervous excitability in frogs (prepared in the manner which physiologists soon came to call the "Galvani preparation") when he observed that under the influence of distant electrical discharges, violent muscle contractions are noted if the lumbar nerves of the animal are touched with metal instruments. It should be related, in this connection, that a few years

---

[4] du Bois-Reymond, E. *Untersuchungen über thierische Elektricität*. 1848, I.

[5] Galvani, A. *De viribus electricitatis in motu musculari commentarius, cum Joannis Aldini dissertatione et notis*. Modena, 1792.

[6] The letter addressed to Carminati by Galvani was first published in the *Giornale Fisico-medico*, 1792, II: 131.

[7] Fulton, J. F. and Cushing, H. *A bibliographical study of the Galvani and the Aldini writings on animal electricity*. Annals of Science, 1936, I: 239.

[8] Galvani, A. *Abhandlung über die Kräfte der thierischen Elektricität auf die Bewegung der Muskeln nebst einigen Schriften der H. H. Valli, Carminati, und Volta über eben diesen Gegenstand*. Translated by D. Johann Mayer, Prague, 1793.

[9] Galvani, A. *Abhandlung über die Kräfte der Electricität bei der Muskelbewegung*. Translated by A. J. von Oettingen. Leipzig, 1894.

[10] Sirol, M. *Galvani et le Galvanisme*. Paris, 1939.

[11] Galvani's use of the electrostatic machine (artificial electricity) in producing muscular contraction is reported in folders of the Manuscripts. The first experiment (*Plic. II, Fasc. A*) is dated November 6, 1780, but this was not the first observation made by Galvani (2). On the top of the sheet of paper he wrote, "Frog prepared in the usual manner."

before, in Bologna, Floriano Caldani (1756) and Giambattista Beccaria (1758) were able to demonstrate electrical excitability in the muscles of dead frogs. At that time the reaction was attributed to the *colpo di ritorno*, an explanation advanced by Galvani himself. Although Galvani was telling his anatomy students[12] that the nervous fluid was animal electricity, he himself was not satisfied fully with the explanation which he was offering, and believed that he had discovered a new phenomenon, which was his greatest contribution.

The significance of the experiment of Galvani was emphasized by Maiorana[13] in his discourse during the Galvani commemoration of 1937. The phenomenon of the *colpo di ritorno*, which (in Galvani's time) could be explained as a simple effect of electrostatic induction, contains the germ of modern wireless telegraphy. "Great things have small beginnings. What in Galvani's hands could move a muscle, brought Marconi's voice across oceans."[14]

In the beginning Galvani investigated the effects of artificial electricity on the nerves and muscles of frogs. Later he performed several experiments on warm-blooded animals with the natural electricity of atmospheric discharges, assisted by his nephew Camillo Galvani. He discovered that natural discharges caused lasting muscular contractions whether the skies were cloudy or clear, from which he concluded that his frog preparation was "an electric current meter through which the electric fluid of nearby bodies passed; the most delicate electrometer yet discovered."[15] But it was in the course of studying the effects of electricity in bright daylight that he made his most valuable discovery. The description of this experiment in one of his Manuscripts (*Fasc. H del Plic. V*) is worthy of quotation. "Accordingly, on an evening early in September 1786, we placed some frogs horizontally on a parapet, prepared in the usual manner by piercing and suspending their spinal cords with iron hooks. The hooks touched an iron plate; behold! a variety of not

---

[12] See: *Alcuni passi estratti dalle Lezioni pubbliche d'Anatomia del cel. Galvani*, which appeared in *Opere edite ed inedite* (2).

[13] Maiorana, Q. *Commemorazione di Luigi Galvani*. Celebrazione del secondo Centenario della nascita di Luigi Galvani. Fasc. I. Bologna, 1938.

[14] This is what was sent in the celebrated communication from the Royal Society of Edinburgh to the University of Bologna on the 200th anniversary of Galvani's birth.

[15] This conclusion appears in *Fasc. A.* of *Plic. IV* of the Manuscripts following notes referring to several experiments.

infrequent spontaneous movements in the frog. If, when they were quiescent, the hook was pressed with the finger against the iron surface, the frogs became excited almost as often as this type of pressure was applied. When this was observed . . ."

At the beginning of the Third Part of the Commentary (the most important part) it is interesting to note[2] that while the manuscript said that the hook piercing the spinal cord of the frog was made of iron (*of the same metal as the railing on which the animal was placed*), in the printed copy the small instrument is described as being made of copper. Galvani noted that the response was more readily obtained with a bimetallic arc than when using a single metal. Subsequently, in the Commentary, he stressed the greater efficacy of heterogeneous over homogenous arcs, which was the basis of what later came to be called Galvanism and is today called electrodynamics.

At first, Galvani believed that metals possessed the property of electrical discharge. From his Manuscripts it appears that the first experiment performed with a metallic arc occurred on September 20, 1786. The observations made on that day and during the month which followed were collected in a folder entitled, *Esperimenti circa l'elettricità de' metalli* and appeared in print on October 30th under the title of *De animali electricitate*.

Soon afterwards, Galvani was strongly convinced of the existence of animal electricity which was discharged by metallic arcs, but he was a thorough investigator and required proof, "for it is easy in experimentation to be deceived, and to think one has seen and discovered what one has desired to see and discover." (Commentary, Part Three). The new observations, made by him on frogs and other animals, led him to believe that a fluid, similar but not identical with the electrical fluid, might flow through the arc. He called this phenomenon *electricitatis excursus*.[16] His theory was finally sum-

---

[16] In the volume *Dell'uso e dell'attività dell'arco conduttore nelle contrazioni dei muscoli* (Anonymous, Bologna, 1794) and in the *Memorie* to Spallanzani (20), the phenomenon was called *torrante elettrica*. Gherardi in his *Rapporto* on Galvani's Manuscripts (2) as well as in his speech to the Academy on February 24, 1842 demonstrated that Galvani was the "true and only author" of *Trattato dell'arco conduttore* and the *Supplemento*. The phenomenon of muscular contraction elicited without metals is described for the first time on pages 5 and 7 of the *Supplemento*. In addition it is stated in the *Trattato* and the *Supplemento* that contractions may occur even at the moment of circuit interruption. Galvani stated that a "constant and continuous current" flows during the entire time the arc is complete.

marized as follows (Commentary, Part Four), "it would perhaps not be an inept hypothesis and conjecture, nor altogether deviating from the truth, which should compare a muscle fiber to a small Leyden jar, or other similar electric body, charged with two opposite kinds of electricity; but should liken the nerve to the conductor, and therefore compare the whole muscle with the assemblage of Leyden jars."

The publication of the Commentary, written in Galvani's lucid and highly expressive prose aroused great interest among scientists in Italy and elsewhere. Every experiment described was repeated to check for accuracy and to determine the meaning of this extraordinary phenomenon. Alessandro Volta, already famous for his important discoveries in electricity, at first seemed to agree with Galvani's explanation of animal electricity; but this acceptance lasted only a few months, for when the idea of contact electricity occurred to him he expressed doubts about Galvani's hypothesis, and embarked on further research which led to the production of electric current from a pile of heterogeneous metals.

The long debate which stemmed from this divergence of opinions, kept alive by ingenious experiments by both Galvani and Volta, represents one of the most memorable and fruitful arguments in the history of science. It reflects the ardent passion which was the glory as well as the torment of these two great spirits. According to Volta, the possibility of exciting muscular contractions with monometallic arcs depended only on the heterogeneity of the substances presented by the contact points of the arc with the muscle through which electricity was generated. To the objections of Volta, Galvani responded with the results of his experiments which in effect marked the beginning of electrophysiology. The first experiment publicly made in 1794 was virtually the discovery of the polarization potential of muscle. When in a nerve-muscle frog preparation the free end of the nerve is laid across the muscle, contraction is seen at the moment of contact. The second experiment, announced in 1797, demonstrated the existence of injury potential in nerves. When two isolated frog legs are placed in contact, if the sectioned surface of the nerve of each is placed on the intact surface of the other, the muscles of each contract when the circuit is closed (that is, when a second contact is established). This experiment conducted without any metal proved that living tissue is generally the seat of electrical currents.

In order to collect new data to support his theory, Galvani investigated the electrical properties of marine torpedoes. Although he was not in good health, Galvani embarked on a tiring sea voyage in May 1795, to Senigallia and Rimini, whence he returned with notes on his daily observations. The pages of this *Taccuino* (Pocket Note-book) reflect the passionate zeal of this great biologist, for they are lively vignettes which arouse admiration and deep affection. This valuable autograph was printed for the first time in 1869.[17] In 1912 the original was purchased by the City of Bologna for the Library of the *Archiginnasio* and was reproduced in facsimile in 1937.[18] A report of his trip to and studies along the Adriatic coast was made by Galvani before the Academy of Sciences of the *Istituto* on February 11, 1796[19] as reported in the *Memoria V Sulla elettricità animale*, addressed to Lazzaro Spallanzani.[20] After differentiating a vigorous autochthonous true electric current in torpedoes, Galvani tried to find out "whether it was the same current as produced in the laboratory, and whether the same conductors could be used for each type." He discovered that "the (electrical) fluid in the nerves of the organs was identical with that of the muscles," and confirmed Girardi's observation[21] that the same nerves supply the dorsal muscles mentioned, with similar "substance, structure and texture."

After Galvani demonstrated that muscular contractions were noted in frogs without the use of metals, Volta postulated that electrical flow was not peculiar to metals alone but also to second class conductors. It was this research of Galvani which brought Volta to

---

[17] *Taccuino delle esperienze del Galvani sulla Torpedine fatte a Senigaglia ed a Rimini l'anno 1795*. Memorie dell'Accademia delle Scienze dell'Istituto di Bologna, 1869, Series II, 9, 177. It is part of the report *Di due preziosi mss. del Galvani sulla Torpedine*, which Gherardi read on May 7, 1868.

[18] *Il Taccuino di Luigi Galvani*. Bologna, 1937.

[19] *Dissertazione accademica del Galvani sulla Torpedine*. Memorie dell'Accademia delle Scienze dell'Istituto di Bologna, 1869, Series II, 9, 163. It was reported together with *Taccuino*, in the Gherardi report (17).

[20] *Memorie sulla elettricità animale di Luigi Galvani P. Prof. di Notomia nella Università di Bologna al celebre Abate Lazzaro Spallanzani Pubblico Professore nella Università di Pavia. Aggiunte alcune elettriche esperienze di Gio. Aldini P. Prof. di Fisica*. Bologna, 1797.

[21] Girardi, M. *Saggio di osservazioni anatomiche intorno agli organi elettrici della Torpedine*. Memorie di Matematica e Fisica della Società italiana, 1768, III: 553.

the invention of the voltaic pile, following which galvanism achieved its great and unexpected usefulness.[22] From a review of the documents of this titanic contest which attracted the attention of the whole of scientific Europe, we can appreciate that their opposing views faithfully represent the true aspect of the facts.

Galvani's merits as a physicist and physiologist obscured his contributions to anatomy, yet his morphological investigations by themselves would have been sufficient to secure his reputation. His first publication[23] dated 1762, discussed the anatomy and pathology of bones. These *Theses*, according to the custom of the times, were publicly discussed by Galvani at the *Archiginnasio* (to enable him to lecture at the University). His first dissertation inserted in the Commentaries of the Academy is dated 1767 and was concerned with bird kidneys.[24] In order to investigate the disposition and thin structure of renal tubules, Galvani caused a natural injection of the tubules by ligating the ureters and in that way anticipated by almost a century, the approach of Hoppe-Seyler and Zaleski. In that paper, for the first time, the three layers of the ureteral walls as well as the peristaltic and antiperistaltic motions of the ureters were described.

In his second dissertation,[25] read before the Academy on February 19, 1767, Galvani reported the results of his experiments on the nasal mucosa in men and several animals, and described in detail the mucous glands and the tubercles situated in the inferior portion of the septum and the anterior portion of the inferior turbinates. He also read several Latin essays[26] before the Academy on the structure and functions of the ear in birds shortly before Scarpa published his famous paper on the round window and secondary tympanum.[27]

---

[22] The relationship between Galvani's discoveries and the subsequent evolution of science is well illustrated by Maiorana (13).

[23] Galvani, A. *De ossibus. These physico-medico-chirugicae* (sic). Bologna, 1762.

[24] Galvani, A. *De renibus atque ureteribus volatilium.* De Bononiensi Scientiarum et Artium Instituto atque Academia Commentarii, 1767, V: 500.

[25] Galvani, A. *Disquisitiones anatomicae circa membranam pituitariam.* This appears in *Opere edite ed inedite* (2).

[26] The first dissertation on this subject was read on May 5, 1768; the sixth and last was read on April 25, 1776. Neither of these dissertations could be found in the Archives of the Academy (3).

[27] Scarpa, A. *De structura fenestrae rotundae auris et de tympano secundario anatomicae observationes.* Modena, 1772.

In this paper published at Modena in 1772, the author credited himself with many of the facts communicated by Galvani between 1768 and 1770.[28] Galvani then gave up his plan of publishing a complete work on this subject, delaying for a future date the publication of observations overlooked by Scarpa,[29] in the Commentaries of the Academy.

Several historians and anatomists have commented on the great value of Galvani's investigations on the ear.[30] He discussed the variation in diameter of the auditory canal, its straight direction, slight depth and different configurations in various kinds of birds. The middle ear canal is treated only sketchily by Scarpa but described in detail by Galvani who compares it to the aqueduct of Falloppia in man and mentions his discovery of a small nerve branch and artery within it. He was the first to write of the bony cavity leading to the oval or round window, which he called the *antevestibolo*. He investigated the function of the two muscles which end and are inserted into the auditory ossicle. He also followed the entire course of the *chorda tympani* by means of a lens. He noted that the cavity of the labyrinth was lined with a dense lucid membrane. In the canal, replacing the cochlea, the presence of a double dividing lamina with a cartilaginous aspect was demonstrated through which a branch of the acoustic nerve travels as far as the apex. He also noted the great size of the semicircular canals and their *colliculi nervei*. Galvani was also the first to discover that the labyrinth is provided with an artery which enters that cavity by an opening situated at the origin of the larger semicircular canal where it divides into several capillaries.

[28] According to many biographers of Galvani and Scarpa, a dispute over the priority of observations on the ear was aroused among the schools of Bologna, Modena, Padua and Pavia. According to Scarpa these observations were made by some of his masters and by many of Morgagni's pupils. According to Galvani, lecturers of the *Studio* of Bologna and professors of Parma were the first to make these observations. This dispute was probably less serious than the published reports would indicate. (Favaro, G. *Antonio Scarpa e l'Università di Modena*. Modena, 1932). When Scarpa was a student he spent his summers in Bologna to obtain practice in surgery. (Favaro, G. *Antonio Scarpa e l'Università di Padova*. Atti R. Ist. ven Sci., Lett. Arti, 1931–1932, II.). This was during the very years in which Galvani was working on the ear. There is probably some connection between these facts.

[29] Galvani, A. *De volatilium aure*. De Bononiensi Scientiarum et Artium Instituto atque Academia Commentarii, 1783, VI: 420.

[30] Medici, M. *Elogio di Luigi Galvani*. Bologna, 1845; Bilancioni, G. *Galvani anatomico dell'orecchio*. Il Valsalva, 1934, X: 545; Castaldi, L. *Nel bicentario della nascita di Luigi Galvani*. Riforma med., 1937, LIII: 937.

He called attention to the *incantesimo* of the heart, a momentary cessation of heart pulsations which he noted in frogs when a needle was inserted into their spinal canals.[31] He saw for the first time, the phenomenon of inhibition, the theory of which later became so important in physiology and psychology.

All of Galvani's writings show exhaustive thoroughness, masterly observation and literary excellence. He was also an eloquent speaker and called upon to deliver speeches during academic ceremonies[32] especially as exemplified in the excellent *De manzoliniana supellectili oratio*[33] given in 1777 at the dedication of the Anatomical Theatre.[34]

Luigi Galvani was born on September 9, 1737, in a house which may still be seen on Via Marconi, 25, in the center of Bologna, into a family which had produced several illustrious men. Upon the completion of his collegiate studies he attended medical classes with some famous teachers of his time: Jacopo Bartolomeo Beccari and Domenico Maria Gusmano Galeazzi. He obtained his degree in medicine and philosophy on July 15, 1759[35] and on May 13, 1761

[31] A few scattered sheets, newly discovered, were added by Gherardi (2) to *Plic. II* of Galvani's Manuscripts. One of these is dated 1778 and records the effect of spinal puncture.

[32] Ten Latin orations delivered during graduation ceremonies from 1790 to 1797 are included in the *Plic. XII* of Galvani's Manuscripts (2). When Galvani's nephew Giovanni Aldini received his degree on November 25, 1782, Galvani delivered an eloquent oration. More than a century later this speech was published by a descendant of Galvani (Galvani, L. *Orazione per la laurea di G. Aldini*. Translated into Italian by Augusto Chiesa. Bologna, 1888).

[33] Galvani, A. *De manzoliniana supellectili* oratio. Bologna, 1777. Anna Morandi was born in Bologna in 1716, married Manzolini and died in 1774. A learned anatomist, she held a chair at the University and became best known for her ability to make wax anatomical figures. The *Stanza* (also called *Camera* or *Gabinetto*) of Anatomy at the Institute later received these figures.

[34] Minor writings of Galvani include: a) *De aeriformibus principiis Thermarum porrectanarum dissertatio*, read before the Academy on November 5, 1789, and published by Michele Medici in "Memorie dell'Accademia delle Scienze dell'Istituto di Bologna, 1851, III: 61; b) *Sentimento del Dottore Luigi Galvani sopra la natura del male da cui sono attaccate le bestie bovine nelle Comunità di Virnignano e Savignano, di Vigo e di Verzuno, di Burzanella e di Montagù Ragazza, e di Camugnano (Provincia di Bologna)*. The manuscript written in 1775 was published by Giambattista Ercolani in the *Giornale di Medicina veterinaria*, 1860, I: 539; c) *Deduzioni sintetiche su l'elettricità animale*, was published on July 7, 1798 by Paolo Predieri in *Memorie dell'Accademia delle Scienze dell'Istituto di Bologna*, 1861, XII: 36; d. *Dissertazione latina sopra l'azione delle mefiti nel corpo animale*, was read before the Academy on April 27, 1797 and published by Silvestro Gherardi in *Memorie dell'Accademia delle Scienze dell'Istituto di Bologna*, 1870, X: 478.

[35] Archivio di Stato di Bologna, Studio. Acta ill. et ex Coll. Phil. et Med. Bononiae from 1753 to 1760, page 94.

he was appointed *alunno* (student) at the Academy of Sciences of the *Istituto*.[36] He practiced medicine and surgery in Bologna hospitals soon after but also found time for anatomical research. He was appointed lecturer *de Rebus medicis* at the *Archiginnasio* he had attended, and on April 28, 1763 was made honorary lecturer.[37] In the years which followed he taught surgery and theoretical anatomy. On June 22, 1768 he became a *Lectura stipendaria* (paid lecturer)[38] and taught medical practice. He became Galeazzi's adjunct in anatomy on December 12, 1775, under whom he taught practical anatomy.[39] He held that office until the year of his death.

Galvani also taught at the *Istituto delle Scienze*. In March of 1766 the Senate of Bologna[40] made him Curator and Demonstrator of the anatomical museum[33] which required him to give lectures and demonstrations of anatomical operations before surgeons, painters and sculptors. On February 26, 1782, that same Senate[41] appointed him Professor of Obstetric Arts at the *Istituto*, a title which he held for sixteen years.[42] In addition to these duties, he taught classes in his home on pathological anatomy and was thus kept busy teaching, investigating, and practicing medicine and obstetrics.

He joined both the Academy of Medicine and Philosophy and several times was appointed rector or rector's councillor of each, and on May 13, 1772[43] as one of the *benedettini* of the Academy of Sciences, its chairman. His moral greatness was in complete harmony with his intellectual stature. Contemporary writers and first biographers describe Galvani as an honest, mild, modest man, polite, charitable to the unfortunate and always a noble and generous friend. Even in trying moments he showed unshakable strength of character. He was a very pious man and showed fervor and reverence in even the most detailed religious observances. According to Vella[44]

[36] Atti delle risoluzioni e dei decreti dell'Accademia dell Scienze dell'Istituto di Bologna, Fasc. 13.

[37] Archivio di Stato di Bologna, Senato. Liber Partitorum from 1762 to 1769, 54: 38.

[38] Ibid. 54: 163.

[39] Ibid. 55: 225.

[40] Ibid. 54: 108.

[41] Ibid. 56: 169.

[42] Bacialli, L. *L'insegnamento della Ostetricia a Bologna dalle origini ad oggi*, (1754 to 1950). Bologna, 1950.

[43] Atti delle risoluzioni e dei decreti dell'Accademia delle Scienze dell'Istituto di Bologna, Fasc. 16.

[44] Vella, L. *Discorso pronunziato all'inaugurazione del monumento a Luigi Galvani*. Bologna, 1879.

religion had become his conscience. This made him interpret his own art as a spiritual mission which he always followed with fraternal love towards the sick.

At his preceptor's house, Galvani met the only daughter of the famous anatomist Galeazzi, Lucia, whom he soon married. This intelligent and learned lady shared many happy and anxious hours with him for almost thirty years.[44] Her death on June 30, 1790[45] was a blow from which he never recovered. His last years were burdened by more than emotional pains for he had the physical pains probably caused by pyloric stenosis.[46]

The most outstanding proof of his strength of character was shown by Galvani during the final year of his life. When an edict of the Cisalpine Republic, created by Napoleon, ordered that all public officials take an oath of allegiance to its constitution, this great patriot refused because he would not subscribe to a formula so contrary to his principles: the oath was atheistic. By refusing to take the oath he lost all his offices at the University and the Institute in April 1798[47] which reduced him to poverty in his last days. Pietro Giordani wrote that "he neither suffocated the voice of conscience, nor made it subservient to profit and ambition, but accepted poverty, losing without protest those academic offices which were his very bread."[48] His fellow citizens, and especially Giovanni Aldini, appealed to the Government to remedy this injustice, and Galvani was restored to his previous offices as emeritus professor, but the decree was announced when death was about to take him. He died at 61 on December 4, 1798, in the house of his birth to which he had returned to live with his brother following the death of his wife. In accordance with his will[49] his body was buried next to that of his *carissima* wife[45], in the *Monastero delle Suore del Corpus Domini.*

---

[45] Lucia Galvani was buried in the *Arca delle Casse* at the Corpus Domini on July 2, 1790. By the will of Luigi Galvani, her body was exhumed and transferred to the burial place near the original tomb. A parchment containing biographical data referring to Lucia Galvani was written in Latin by Galvani and placed in her tomb at the time. This parchment, placed in a lead container was found when her remains were exhumed in 1873. Dino Zucchini found a copy of the original in 1937 (Zucchini, D. *Elogio dettato da Luigi Galvani in morte della moglie Lucia Galeazzi.* Bologna, 1938.

[46] Medici, M. *Elogio di Luigi Galvani.* Bologna, 1845.

[47] Al principio di Fiorile Anno VI, according to Venturoli (2).

[48] Giordani, P. *Opere.* Vol. II. Florence, 1857.

[49] Malagola, C. *Luigi Galvani nell'Universita, nell (Istituto e nell) Accademia delle Scienze di Bologna.* Bologna, 1879.

There the two bodies remained neglected until 1873 when on the 30th of October, the City of Bologna transferred their remains to a marble sarcophagus built in a special vault of the Church adjoining the monastery.[50]

During World War II, Sister Luisa, of the Convent of Saint Catherine where the Galvanis were buried, had a premonition that the burial vault would be struck by an aerial bomb. She collected the remains in small metal vessels and transferred them to the Church of San Luca atop nearby *Osservanza* Hill. A bomb demolished the original vault. On July 27, 1947 the remains were returned to the Convent where they await proper reburial in the badly damaged holy site.

It is not civic apathy which has as yet prevented Bologna from gathering into a worthy resting place the bones of its most famous son, who, by devoting himself to the search for truth, has given his name to all the languages of the world.

GIULIO C. PUPILLI
Director of the Institute of Human Physiology
University of Bologna, Italy

February 2, 1953.

[50] The Corpus Domini Church is commonly called *della Santa*, in commemoration of Saint Catherine of Vigri, protectress of the arts, buried there.

Concerning the Origin and Development of the Theory
of Animal Electricity

Dissertation by
Giovanni Aldini

Dissertation of Giovanni Aldini[1]
Concerning the Origin and Development
of the Theory of Animal Electricity

I. It is my purpose to portray briefly what was the origin, what the development, of animal electricity, what the experiments performed under the leadership of Galvani, and to emphasize those things which either preceded or followed that man's industry. Although animal electricity did not have the same beginnings as common electricity, nevertheless it has undergone not dissimilar vicissitudes. That famous discovery of amber by Thales of Miletus[2] long lay neglected until the fortunate age of Beccarius, Delibard, Wilson, Epinus, and of him who is worth them all, Franklin, illuminated it by their labors, the age which, with iron rods placed aloft, did not fear even the thunderbolts of indignant Jove. Nevertheless, in the memory of the fathers also, many observed phenomena were corrupted, partly by the perversity of the times, partly by the fables of poets.

II. It escapes no one what Cicero, Livy[3] and Valerius Maximus have handed down to memory concerning the flames observed about the head of Servius Tullius; but the reputation of that prophetic

[1] Distinguished physicist, nephew of Galvani. Born at Bologna, April 10, 1762; died at Milan, January 17, 1834. In 1798 he succeeded Canterzani as Professor of Physics at the University of Bologna.

Etymologically and genealogically the name Galvani is of French Keltic or Gaelic origin. In the form of Galvain or Gauvain it was widely diffused during the early medieval centuries through Brittany and Normandy. Thence by Keltic migration it made its way to Greater Britain; to Lesser Britain in the form of the Irish Galvin and Gavin; and then to Scotland in the form of Gawain. The most famous bearer of the name in this Scottish form was of course Gawain, the son of King Lot of Lothian and Orkney, one of the most celebrated heroes of King Arthur's Round Table. Finally at the Norman conquest of Sicily in the eleventh century, the name and heritage were transferred to Italian soil and there became established as Galvani. It is interesting that there is this hereditary and linguistic link between Arthurian romance and this pioneer of electricity.

[2] First of the Seven Sages of Greece, B.C. 636 to 546. He was the first to observe that amber, when rubbed, attracts light bodies.

[3] Titus Livius: Historia Rerum Romanorum: Book I., Cap. XXXIX, 1. "Eo tempore in regia prodigium visum eventuque mirabile fuit: puero dormienti, cui Servio Tullio fuit nomen, caput arsisse ferunt multorum in conspectu."

fire had so spread among the ancients that Virgil[4] also celebrated in his verses Iulus, with the crown of his head surrounded by harmless flames. From Hermolaus Barbarus and our own Aldrovandus[5] we have heard that ravens in their pernicious flight bear aloft a flaming beak in the midst of tempests; that eagles, at the fall of thunderbolts are so surrounded with unwonted light that they shine gleaming in the sky like planets. Hence perhaps prophets have considered that bird as sacred to Jove and minister of the thunder bolt;[6] which interpretation was strongly approved by Guenau de Montbeillard, who chiefly insisted on this, that the fables themselves derive their origin from some fact.

But from all these things, electricity could be deemed not as innate in animals but merely communicated, whose action long before had been expressed both by stars gleaming about the spars and yards of sailors, and by fires falling into the night-watches of soldiers, which Caesar[7] recalls when he reports that through the night the spear-points of the fifth legion "burned of their own accord." Therefore, setting aside electricity communicated to animals, we will pursue that which is regarded as innate, first in animals generally, and then in man.

III. Immediately there present themselves the celebrated experiments of Gordon, with which he embellished the well-known electricity of the cat. For using insulating substances he collected as much electricity as, conducted to the upper surface of vinous spirits, produced very prompt flaming. Hartmann and Dubois, by making light attrition, caused notable electric attraction in the feathers of a bird which they call Kakatois (cockatoo). What shall I say of the Torpedo which, safeguarded by its electrical explosions from injury

---

[4] Aeneid II, 682.
> "Ecce levis summo de vertice visus Iuli
> Fundere lumen apex, tactuque innoxia mollis
> Lambere flamma comas, et circum tempora pasci."

[5] Ulisse Aldrovandi. A celebrated naturalist of Bologna, 1522–1607 A.D. He wrote an ornithology in three volumes, and three more treating of insects and mollusca; his botany embraced sixty folios.

[6] Cf. Hor. Od IV, 4, 1–4
> "Qualem ministrum fulminis alitem,
> Cui rex deorum regnum in aves vagas
> Permisit expertus fidelem
> Juppiter in Ganymede flavo."

[7] De Bello Africano. VI.

by larger fishes, converts those fleeing in consternation to its own nutrition. The most recent observations of Walsh and Spallanzani have made known the properties of Torpedo, ascertained by Aristotle and Pliny. One of them recognized in it the structure of the magic square,[8] electricity having been detected on its back from excess, on its belly from deficiency; the other, at his preference, prohibited concussions by interposing an insulating body, and noted succussion not only in the Torpedo submerged in water, but also in the foetus while enclosed in the maternal uterus. Vanderlot and Bajonius discovered phenomena cognate to the Torpedo in the electric Gymnotis (eels) living along the coasts of Surinam and Cayenne. A few years from then, moreover, a family mated two species[9] of electric fishes with itself; but if others are added by the industry of the physicists, there will be new electric swarms of fishes, whose incursions will be highly hostile to the swimming inhabitants of the ocean.

IV. But there are not lacking terrestrial animals who seem to rival to a high degree the electric virtue of the Torpedo. The celebrated anatomist Cotunius with a knife cut the epigastrium of a live mouse firmly grasped in his left hand, and suddenly had a very violent concussion, which was transmitted with such force from his arm to his shoulders and then to his head that immediately he had to marvel at the phenomenon and throw the mouse away. But I think the glory of the newly discovered electricity lightened for a whole quarter-hour and more the pain incurred in his head and arms. The industry of Vassalius and of others confirmed the observations of Cotunius.

V. It would have been thoughtless of nature to deprive men of the beneficent action of electric fluid, which she had granted most abundantly to brute beasts. It had already been ascertained that Camusius had prepared himself an electrophore, from dried nerves. The bones of the head, on rubbing, have often shown me no slight electricity. Saussurius, famous for many physical and mechanical inventions, excited electricity in the living man by the lightest attrition: after taking a short walk, he wished to ascend an insulated surface, and, having applied his hand to a light electrometer, was immediately amazed at the divergent wires. Sauvagesius reports in

[8] A name sometimes given to the quadrant electrometer or electroscope.
[9] One of these is called "trembleur," the other is ascribed to the genus "tetrodon."

his treatise on hemiplegia, that the lower limbs of certain men gave out an electric vapor after walking. Fougeroux, Bovilletus, and also our own Laura Bassia,[10] have often noticed little flames breaking out from human bodies, either when lingerie was being changed or when silk garments were being donned in a very dark chamber. When Symmerius doffed his stockings, he saw vivid electricity flowing from his legs: but when two silk stockings by which the same leg was covered, one white the other black, were separated, opposite electricity was immediately generated, so that indeed the former became positively electric, the latter negatively. But these phenomena I should truly prefer to derive from friction, particularly silk, than from native human electricity.

VI. Animal electricity has not rarely been seen to have dwelt in intent eyes, studious of things. Bartholinus,[11] in his well-known treatise concerning the light of animals, mentions a man whom anyone could easily recognize because more light shone from his eyebrows. Bartholinus adds that the eyes of hydrophobes have many times become ignited, so that on that account he thinks it by no means fabulous which the historians relate of Alexander the Great, whom, in the midst of battle, the ardor of glory had so permeated that his eyes also seemed to blaze. But, truly, let happier natures pursue remote and lofty conjectures. Electricity has greatly pleased the gravest physicists and physiologists in explaining the phenomena of hydrophobes: they have not hesitated even from the optic nerves, electricized by sudden rubbing, to derive distinct circles with various colors of light, or bright points, commonly called stars, which are excited when the eyes are struck by a sudden blow.

VII. Animal electricity has sometimes been regarded as a most pernicious cause of some of the gravest crises of life. Hence those very unfortunate explosions described by Masseius, Bianchinus,[12]

---

[10] Laura Maria Caterina Bassi, a learned Italian lady of Bologna, 1711 to 1778, a doctor and professor of experimental science at Bologna University. She married a physician, Giuseppe Verrati, and had several children.

[11] Gaspard Bartholinus, a learned Swede, of Malmöe, 1585–1630, who studied at the Universities of Copenhagen, Rostock, and Wittemberg, and became successively Professor of Medicine and of Divinity.

Thomas Bartholinus, son of Gaspard, born at Copenhagen in 1617. He studied medicine at Leyden; studied also at Paris, Montpellier, Padua, and Basel. He was Professor of Anatomy at Copenhagen from 1647 to 1661, studying particularly the lymphatics, and the vulvo-vaginal glands which were named for him. He died on December 4, 1680.

[12] Francesco Bianchini, a noted Italian astronomer and antiquary, born at Verona, De-

and Wilmer, which, while men were enjoying a clear sky, suddenly brought them to horrible death, pulverized to powder; these bedtime thunderbolts, as they call them, many physicists refer to the same animal electricity: but truly we should be less disturbed if, in explaining so great a matter, they would not reject the association of other forces. But it is easy for us to refrain from these conjectures, lest, by ascribing all phenomena to electricity, confidence finally be diminished in those in which it is really concerned. Let us therefore pursue what belongs to our intention, those things which merely evince the certain existence of animal electricity.

VIII. Bridonius, in a written communication to the Royal Academy of London, discloses a delicate electricity of the hairs. Every device looks to this end, that there should be two men, of whom one sits on a conducting surface and displays to the other, who is insulated, the countless hairs on his chest to be separated. Thereupon the insulated man becomes as it were the conductor of an animal electricity machine: hence from him vivid sparks streamed, whence vinous spirit was ignited and a Leyden jar charged, which greatly moved those who were present at the observation. But in this, two things are particularly to be guarded against, one that no powder or ointments be used by the hair for its nourishment, the other that when sparks are to be sought, the experiment be done in an extremely dark chamber, lest the brilliance of the animal electricity excited be obscured by the external light. Although these things pertain to the more recent theory of electric vapor, yet they have not been able after many years to displace the sagacity of the celebrated Mairani who had adequately explained the electricity of hairs by his observations.

IX. Electric vapor, hitherto elicited, was not limited to human integuments but also dominated widely in the internal human mechanism. Vassalius and Volta, with the highly mobile electrometer of Tiberius Cavallus, discovered that a large amount of electricity is associated with the urine of man. Michael Pushkin,[13] when Tobolski was in good health, communicated an electric spark to those who touched him. Lassinius relates that in Florence he perceived phe-

---

cember 13, 1662; died at Rome, March 2, 1729. He was educated at Padua, and devoted himself especially to the classics and mathematics. His last work was a series of observations on the planet Venus, entitled "Hesperi et Phosphori Nova Phaenomena."

[13] Younger brother of the poet, Alexander Pushkin.

nomena in a Russian man closely cognate to the electric property of the Torpedo: Gaubius teaches in his pathology that he had observed this in a certain patient long before. Behold, transmitted even to human beings, wonderful properties which nature seemed to have imparted to the Torpedo alone!

X. The subjects which we have thus far pursued, great and important though they are, seem nevertheless to be far distant from the recently detected Galvanic electricity. Certainly the electrophores made of dry nerves or bones do not prove it, nor sparks breaking from hairs, or limbs, or integuments. For since almost all bodies destitute of moisture in some way become insulating, and since skin and hairs evince a non-conductile nature, there is no reason to wonder why some electricity arises with attrition, which ought more truly to be called artificial than natural. In the previous observations, Saussurius declared the power of artificial attrition, who failed to get electric attraction in a man who was insulated by no clothing causing attrition. But that the remaining phenomena, which we were discussing, it should appear, are not to be confounded with animal electricity, it should be more deeply explored, and more diligent investigation made into Galvani's theory.

XI. Now Galvani's *Commentary* has four parts, of which the first and second explain the power of communicated electricity, the third describes electricity intrinsic in animals and producing muscular motions, and the fourth proposes some conjectures and corollaries. As for what pertains to the first and the second part, although it had become known to physiologists that artificial electricity was most potent for exciting muscular motions, they had been accustomed to apply it to the muscles to be excited. But, what no one had attempted before Galvani, was now accomplished by his sagacity and ingenuity, that we may have muscles disposed to contraction by the mere passage of a spark, although they may be either situated far remote from the conductor, or surrounded on all sides with sheets of glass. And those contractions in enclosed frogs remote from the conductor are excited by the action of either artificial or atmospheric electricity. And yet, while Beccaria's[14] celebrated theory

[14] Giovanni Battista Beccaria, celebrated Italian mathematician and physicist. Born at Mondovi, Piedmont, October 3, 1716; died at Turin, May 27, 1781. He was Professor of Physics at the Universities of Palermo, Rome, and of Turin, and especially noted for his researches in electricity. He was elected a Fellow of the Royal Society of London in May, 1755.

of electric vapor stood valid, the existence of intrinsic and native animal electricity could always by strict reasoning be derived from the action of extrinsic electricity. For muscles immersed, for example, in an atmosphere of extrinsic positive electricity, cannot themselves escape being electrified unless they find the opposite electricity, or exude electricity introduced into them; while this is happening, muscular motions are excited. Therefore communicated electricity does not itself produce the contraction, but, disturbing from its equilibrium the electricity in the muscles, conduces to the production of contraction. So that from the first and the second part of the *Commentary* we learn how often the electricity in muscles is itself disturbed and moves the muscle.

XII. But if perchance to anyone the proposed reasoning should seem too presumptuous, let him not therefore despise the experiments on which it depends, or especially on that name, which first showed Galvani the distinguished pathway of discovering intrinsic animal electricity. Therefore there is no reason why we should seek from selected conjectures that which the third part of the *Commentary* vindicates on its own right by new observations, and which is supported and demonstrated by experiments. Hence it will readily appear that to the same term of animal electricity, which we have used above, ought to be added hereafter a new force and significance according to Galvani's discoveries. For he himself is our authority that only that should be considered true animal electricity which is spontaneously excited in warm or cold-blooded animals, with no approach of artificial electricity, no attrition, and no percussion, which accompanies the final functions of life, and which has between muscles and nerves an easy and calculated course, flow, and circuit. But to this animal electricity is entrusted that noblest duty, that it should supply the functions of the animal economy and accomplish the muscular movements, of which the former could easily be inferred from the affiliated phenomena of the Torpedo and other animals, but the latter is wholly a new consequence of Galvani's observations.

XIII. But all experiments finally come down to this: that, if all action of extrinsic electricity be excluded, if the nerves and muscles are intact and only a metal arc is applied, vigorous contractions occur, which fail completely, if one end of the arc is wrapped in an insulating covering. But those precautions which we provide for ourselves for assisting the action of artificial electricity, the same augment to a remarkable degree the power of animal electricity also. It is truly amazing how much various metallic armatures placed on nerves and muscles assisted Galvani to extract animal electricity. Not merely one, but a twofold, electricity dominates in the animal machine, by excess and by defect, and if, by an artificial arc, they are brought into an equilibrium, then muscular motions cease. In living animals the lack of an artificial arc is supplied by animal humor, suitable in the first instance to convey electricity and bring it to an equilibrium. But if this principle, which flows through friendly conducting bodies, whose too rapid excursion is checked by insulating bodies, which obeys the law of equilibrium, if it is not electric, what will be hereafter the bodies in which we think the electric principle resides?

XIV. But electricity cannot be propagated through bodies of different conductivity, without experiencing some difficulty of transit. Hence Galvani was aided by armatures prepared from different metals, chiefly for the extraction of animal electricity. To him, scrutinizing the more intimate cause of so great a phenomenon, it seemed that he should have recourse to certain as it were chemical properties of electric vapor. The more recent physicists consider electricity harboring in bodies just like a fixed fire, latent heat, phlogiston, or caloric. In their opinion a certain electricity is present, which contributes as an element to the intimate composition of bodies, and cannot produce its own effects unless it is freed from the bonds of closest connection and even of established affinity: hence in electric vapor phenomena occur analogous to those which Wilkie, Blake, and Crawford have recently brought forward concerning latent fire and the varying aptitude of bodies for containing heat. Truly the diversity of metals, which is so potent in augmenting contractions, confers great probability on alleged suspicion. Leaves of gold-foil, prepared with other metal armatures combined, not rarely excite little or no electricity in animals. But this very varied faculty itself, which metals have for receiving and exciting electric vapor, what else does it indicate, if not that bodies are so prepared by their own nature to receive electricity into themselves diversely? How indeed, if two bodies are endowed with the same capacity, as they say, is warmth in equal degree established at an equilibrium in both? So, if homogeneous metals are used, that is no reason why the electricity should betake itself to one more eagerly than to the other, so that on that account, no effort being devoted to equilibrium, no more violent contraction also should arise.

The highly ingenious Thouvenel[15] seems to apply his mind to the proposed conjectures, for he reports at the same time that he has very often observed animal electricity excited in men, who, in accordance with his well-known method, were standing in metal mines. But obviously it is difficult to define to what metal you would assign the foremost part in evolving animal electricity. Nevertheless the illustrious Volta,[16] guided by the most accurate observations, devised a definite classification of metals, which he reduces to three groups: the first includes mercury, gold, silver, and platinum; the second iron, bronze, and copper; and finally tin and lead.

XV. But the study of experimentation in animal electricity was not limited to the confines of Bologna but, spreading more widely in every direction, extended far to foreign Academies also. So that animal electricity which we have pursued above first in brute beasts, then in man, now again in the same order presents itself to be explained by the observations of Galvani. Birds, fishes, very many reptiles display electricity conspicuously.

If an eel is cut transversely, as the most expert observations of Eusebius Valla and Mesinus report, and the spinal cord armatured, immediately the tail trembles vehemently for thirty minutes, then with perceptibly weakened motion, and finally comes to rest when forty-five minutes have not yet elapsed: the armatured head of an eel gave sluggish but longer contractions, which appeared for fifty minutes.

In two tenches, with the spinal cord armatured near the head, the fins were moved five or six times, but after two minutes afforded no

[15] "Metals, and also mines, have proper or spontaneous atmospheres of electricity, which differ among themselves by their intensity, and are even opposite in relation to their determinations, effluent or affluent, centrifugal and centripetal, positive and negative, or mixed: and consequently mines and metals ought not to be considered solely as simple conducting bodies, or conductors of communicated artificial electricity, but as true motor means, excitators or condensers of spontaneous or natural electricity, a property which they possess also to very different degrees." Letter from Thouvenel to Amoretti.

[16] Count Alessandro Volta of Como. Born February 18, 1745. Died at Paris March 5, 1827. Professor at Como and Pavia. Inventor of the electrophore, the electroscope, the condenser, and the voltaic pile.

motion. The wings of a chaffinch were slightly contracted for three minutes, but not so the legs. In a newborn cat, motion was obtained only in the forelegs for a quarter of an hour. In a dog stricken to death with a pinch of pear-powder, the four legs having been prepared and insulated, contractions were excited when a metallic arc was applied: the hyoglossus and genioglossus muscles trembled violently, but the laryngeal muscles, being prepared with the well-known armature, far less. Lizards and turtles afford equal phenomena; then insects also, and almost all kinds of animals were subjected to the same observation with no different result.

XVI. We recalled that vipers had not yet been tried for first examination, and we were perhaps principally attracted by this, because from their peculiar structure they seemed to promise the most electricity: the outcome did not deceive or fail our preconceived expectation. Their integuments having been reflected, the vipers, indued along the vertebrae with a tinfoil armature, produced vigorous muscular motions with a metallic arc. But the natural movements of vipers, and the violent spontaneous contortions excited in the whole body, seemed to afford some suspicion and ambiguity in animal electricity. Therefore, in order that I might determine whether the excited motions were really electric, I cut the spinal cord transversely in several places, and having made an armature on the nerve-filaments, which are very numerous along the vertebrae, I saw constant muscular movements, which lasted a long time, if the animal moisture were maintained. That I finally remedied, so that the armature close to the vertebrae was somewhat extended outside them by an insulating body; and from this it resulted that, when an arc was applied to the tin armature and to the silver plate, vigorous contractions occurred from intact nerves and muscles. When we practised the same method in the country, we transferred to the cut section of a dead snake, whose length exceeded two feet. But if the vertebrae were armatured and an arc applied, not one, but repeated, and as it were perpetual, contractions arose most violently.

XVII. But, not to go too far afield, I will mention here the noblest invention of Volta, whereby he applied a harmless method of safeguarding the life of any animals and at the same time of experimenting with electricity. Hereafter, therefore, for any comparison of animal electricity, there will be no need of sacrificing any victims, or of reflecting integuments and separating nerves with bloody hands: it will be sufficient that spry, living frogs should sit on a silver plate, indued along the vertebral column with a tin armature. For when an arc is applied, contractions immediately are most vigorous. We placed frogs on a silver plate, with a silver armature also applied along the vertebral column; no contractions arose: and the same result occurred when a living frog was equipped with a double armature of tin-foil to his nerves and to his muscles.

XVIII. But it must be thought that the electric principle, that it may be easily understood from those things which we shall soon submit, was not added by accidental causes, but was intentionally implanted by nature: and we see that the power of this principle is so great that poisons themselves can quickly destroy life, but can by no means extinguish animal electricity. Vallius shut up several animals in various containers, so that he compelled them to inhale the more pernicious gaseous fluids; sometimes he employed inflammable, sometimes nitrous or other mephitic gas; never was animal electricity destroyed. One gas, contaminated by combustion of sulphur, proved very noxious to animal electricity, and this perhaps on account of the injuries which the elements of the muscle fibers had sustained while it was acting.

Moreover, in some frogs, killed by the violent shock of a Leyden jar, no changes in animal electricity occurred; but it always survived when opium, powdered nicotine, or arsenic was administered to frogs.

Galvani also several years later pursued the influence of opium on animal electricity in a Dissertation which he delivered in the Academy of the Institute of Sciences. Frogs, as is gathered from this, when opium is administered either in the stomach or in the abdominal cavity or even introduced within the cerebrum, after a great lethargy is excited, were affected with violent convulsions, either from a slight tremor of the surface upon which they were resting or from the contact of some body. These phenomena also (which is indeed surprising) were not lacking, when the head was cut off before the administration of the opium.

XIX. But it is pleasant to disclose to what end the physicists and physiologists have undertaken so many labors and ingenious attempts. For since man is the chief of all animals, and since previously so many victims had been sacrificed principally for the sake of discovering his electricity, it was worth while that we should have human electricity explored and revealed in fact and not by conjecture. Therefore to Galvani nothing was more important than that with surgical dexterity, in the public hospital of Saint Ursula, he should subject an amputated arm and foot to his experiments. Wherefore an armature was placed on exposed nerves and muscles, so that the nerves communicated with mercury, the muscles with tepid water. When a metal arc was carried from a muscle to the nerves vigorous contractions suddenly arose; but it was ascertained by experiment that it is not nerves, but that by its mere contact with the nerves, the same fairly strong contractions are excited, which very thing had been detected also elsewhere in the lamb, in the calf, and in other animals, especially the warm-blooded. But in order that it might become known to Galvani that the cause of those muscular motions was contained in electricity, he armatured the nerves sometimes with glass, sometimes with resin, sometimes with substances woven of silk: immediately all contraction was arrested. Again he had recourse to the customary armature, and applied the metallic arcs to the insulated nerves, and, to the utmost admiration of those who were present, saw the digits of the foot and the hand, as often as the arc was applied, not merely contract, but relax. It ought not to be passed over in silence that our author had obtained more notable contractions, particularly when he applied armature to the smaller nerve branches. But contractions of the foot far surpassed those which were observed in the hands, either because the feet possess more notable nerves or because the hand tested had suffered more damage from longer disease.

XX. The fortunate outcome of surgical operations in the Hospital brought a persistent patient, suffering from an inveterate ulcer in his foot, to such a point that, changing his plan, he surrendered his foot for amputation with surgical dexterity. Hence a new opportunity was given of testing animal electricity. Therefore, following custom, since we had previously debated together the method of undertaking the experiment, I betook myself to Galvani to the Hospital where, from the beginning of our observations, the thing turned out contrary to our expectation. For when the nerves and several muscles had been exposed, and various kinds of armature had been tried, not only on the larger but also on the smaller nerve-trunks, contractions were lacking, so that I wondered and almost complained at so great variation from experiments previously undertaken. Meantime it was reported that that form of disease had existed in the foot for seventeen years, that the foot, almost wholly consumed by horrible emaciation, had lost almost all motions, along with sensation: and already there were concretions here and there, rough and very hard, and livid integuments, and the whole aspect of the foot was such that those professors of surgery who were then present, having taken consideration of all these things, thought that animal electricity was not to be expected. Nevertheless, although so many obstacles had arisen, there still persisted in my mind some hope of observing electricity, which I could not cast away unless first all ways of testing had been thoroughly explored, and the thing had always turned out the same way; and I did not regret the decision I had taken.

For when a layer of callous and fatty substance[17] had been removed from the sole of the foot, a nerve from the common nerve of the foot[18] presented itself relatively free from injury: moreover, when this nerve was armatured, vigorous contractions occurred there to the nearest toes, (just as Galvani had noted), on the mere application of a metallic arc to the nerves. Moreover we placed the armatured nerve first on mercury, next on a silver surface, next on gold—always very vigorous contractions arose; it is indeed remarkable how much metals of this sort contribute to the assistance of animal electricity. These observations having been made, I again summoned with a more felicitous outcome the companions of my experiment, whom I had previously dismissed; nay, while I was greatly admiring the animal electricity, I drew the reflected integuments back into place, so that they covered the separated muscles and nerves, and I took care that, by sprinkling rags with water, the internal moisture of those parts should be preserved as much as possible, so that thence it might be permitted to learn the durability of animal electricity. Wherefore, after two hours had elapsed, I betook myself again to the Hospital and, the armature having been arranged, it was possible for some weakened contraction still to be seen, which, gradually languishing, was shortly extinct.

[17] Presumably and probably the plantar aponeurosis.
[18] Medial plantar branch of the tibial.

XXI. Sulzer[19] an industrious man, had already noticed many years ago that, if two sheets of different metal were alternately applied on the tongue, a certain taste is produced, like that which accompanies the sulphate of iron; and he thought that the metal dissolved by the tongue claims for itself no part in this. That phenomenon, as the times went, it was endeavored to explain by a certain vibration excited, of one metal, or of the other, or even of both, which, striking the nerves of the tongue, produced some sensation in taste. The illustrious Volta first of all referred Sulzer's observation to the theory of animal electricity, and embellished it so that he seems almost to have made it his own. Moreover, almost for this reason, there arose an investigation which subsequently illuminated a most useful truth. Namely nerves, joined to conducting bodies, pour out an electric vapor which, if it should be restored to the muscles to which it was going, will excite either a contraction or some impression. Therefore nerves should be sought in man which lie so extrinsic that they can easily be armatured with metallic foil: in Sulzer's observation, the tongue afforded these, which, by its moisture, provides a most convenient path for latent electricity. Hence, if tin-foil is fitted to the tip of the tongue and a silver substance to its dorsum, when an arc is made between both armatures, electricity is produced there, which excites only the most delicate vapor, sometimes distinct of flowing acid, sometimes even it imitates a disagreeable sensation: this experiment can most conveniently be done by carrying a silver body, covered with tin, from the dorsum of the tongue to its tip.

XXII. We ought not to pass over here the ingenious suspicion, which has arisen or rather been renewed, which had been already advanced before against Sulzer's observations. Truly, although the power of the saliva for dissolving many substances is great, it is very doubtful whether by chance it would join to itself any particles which would excite the sensation of a definite taste. In order that I

---

[19] Johann Georg Sulzer, a Prussian-Swiss philosopher and professor of aesthetics. He was born at Winterthür, Switzerland, October 5, 1720; and died at Berlin, February 27, 1779. His chief work is his "General Theory of the Fine Arts." In his "New Theory of the Pleasures," he says: "If one joins two pieces, one of lead and the other of silver, in such a way that the two edges make the same surface, and if one approximates them on the tongue, one will perceive from them some taste, fairly approximating the taste of sulphate of iron. Whereas each piece separately gives no trace of this taste. The only probability is that from this junction of the two metals, there occurs some solution of one or of the other, and that the dissolved particles insinuate themselves into the tongue."

might avert as much of that suspicion as was in me, after applying the customary armature to the tip of the tongue, I applied a metal arc interrupted with insulating substance: but rarely slight, and generally no taste arose, which on the contrary, merely considering the saliva dissolving metal, would always have been expected. While I was meditating these things, I learned from a most welcome messenger that the illustrious Volta, by a new and most ingenious experiment looked forward to the security of his observations; for he accomplished the production of tastes, even though all communication of the tongue with metal was cut off.

Therefore he immersed the tip of the tongue into a level of water, in which he had placed a scrap either of tin or of paper covered with tin: when a metal arc was carried from the middle of the tongue to the tin layer, the sensation of an acid taste was excited, which continued to be felt, as long as the contact lasted. That, in the proposed experiment, the certain action of electric vapor might be better confirmed, we substituted oil of almonds for water: when the arc was employed, according to custom, no taste arose. Hence it seems that it can be inferred that the tongue perceives the taste not of dissolved metal but of the electricity running out through it.

XXIII. Moreover, the diversity of metals (as we have carefully noted) produces great varieties in striking upon the organ of taste. Armatures, prepared from silver and from tin, are most suitable for producing tastes. With homologous metals, the action of animal electricity is either diminished or wholly prevented: wherefore, if a silver armature is applied to the tip of the tongue and to its dorsum, no taste is excited; the same thing happens, if you use tin on both sides. But by experimenting, we discovered that this is least suitable for exciting the impression of taste, that the arc should extend from the armatured tip of the tongue to the dorsum. For if from either the arm or the foot immersed in water, or merely from the water-level in which they are, an arc is made to the tip of the tongue covered with tin, vivid taste is immediately excited; but perhaps it will be even more vivid, if the whole animal machine is immersed in water and a metal arc employed, which by its thickness and length in some way invites animal electricity, and can drain it more conveniently. But, leaving these of ours, let us revert to the most illustrious observations of Volta.

XXIV. Great phenomena have followed the taste excited in the tongue by animal electricity, and from these the most ingenious corollaries have derived. For it was ascertained that, by changing the armatures in turn, the tastes are changed also, so that some times the taste becomes not acid, but bitter and burning, which formerly came very near an alkaline nature. These things having been perceived, Volta readily changed to this opinion, so that he thinks it is completely confirmed by the new experiments that there resides in metals the power not merely of conducting but of exciting electricity. Wherefore now, indeed, and deservedly, a distinguished man is to be congratulated, because, if I may say so, he has amplified the domain of animal electricity, although he has applied it not to performing muscular motions but also to producing sensation. For the nerves which serve not only motion, but also sensation, obey animal electricity, so that on this account the mind, with its own safety as a judge, excites either motion or sensation. Hence Volta, having removed the entire tongue from a lamb, and made a double armature, and applied one to the nerves at the root of the tongue, the other to the corresponding muscles, as soon as an arc was applied, obtained very prompt muscular motions. These were the experiments of animal electricity instituted in brute beasts and in man, which anyone will easily understand differ widely from those which had preceded the industry of Galvani.

XXV. In the fourth part of Galvani's *Commentary*, he reasons from certain and explored facts to probable conclusions and conjectures, prepared with all sagacity and industry. To anyone weighing carefully the experiments of the first and second part, it will be clearly convenient to explain the remarkable influence of atmospheric electricity on the animal economy.

Moreover, as Bartholinus teaches, nature seems to have used two media particularly for communicating electricity to the animal economy. First she causes that the universal integuments of the human body should abound with innumerable pores, by which electric fluid may be communicated to animals, whether it were from excess in the atmosphere or from deficiency in the body. Further she provides that, by means of respiration, a new supply of electricity is constantly taken to the lungs, where, as if having found a convenient secretory organ, it is extracted from the air, with which it was combined.

XXVI. Moreover, in accordance with the varied ratio of equilibrium whereby internal animal electricity may be related to extrinsic communicated electricity, it is necessary that the influx of atmospheric electricity should be varied. Hence it will appear why, when a great storm has arisen in heaven, or immense rains have fallen, sometimes the animal machine becomes more active, sometimes in certain patients the symptoms of their malady become more severe. And it will not seem surprising, as reported by Woodward, that certain men have existed, who, before thunderbolts, seemed to suffer immense anguish, and felt their precordia oppressed, and were even compelled to vomit. Beccaria relates that he knew a certain man named Maceas, who, when the sky lightened and thunder rampaged, was seized with most distressing attacks of epilepsy. "Hence lethargy is easily perceived," says Gardiner, "on certain definite days in which artificial electricity is excited with great difficulty." For lassitude, sadness, melancholy, and hysterical manifestations, at certain definite times especially indicate and openly demonstrate that all nervous diseases have relationship with the atmosphere. But the influx of atmospheric electricity is not always harmful and to be feared. The more abundant transpiration of communicated electricity produced can be beneficial, and the prompter and more expeditious excursion of the humors can be of the greatest advantage, to the animal economy. Hence, with a serene sky and placid electricity, we also enjoy, as I may say, a certain most welcome alacrity of our powers, which we do not experience when lower electric clouds hang over us.

XXVII. Now it is extremely difficult to define and determine whether the action of atmospheric electricity thus far considered derives merely from one law of equilibrium, or from other causes also. Mahoney introduced a new sort of rebounding electricity, which nature had previously demonstrated by the conspicuous phenomena of thunderbolts. It is stated in meteorological histories that men have often been destroyed by a thunderbolt which they were watching at some distance as it roared in heaven. In Bennet's most delicate electrometer we have most conveniently observed rebounding electricity, with the physicist J. B. Venturius, in different metallic leaves placed under it, whose further remarkable properties he so pursued that he easily transferred it to explain phenomena which are propounded in the first and second part of Galvani's commentary. With other experiments also, initiated in the same Bennet's electrometer, he thinks he can determine the reason why the contact of a metallic body should move inherent electricity in animals.

XXVIII. But with new knowledge of animal electricity hereafter, and investigation of certain symptoms, some light will necessarily arise for the cure or palliation of certain diseases. Tetanus, epilepsy, convulsions, various diseases of the nerves, as Galvani notes, exhibit many phenomena which demand an understanding of electricity. Surely, if electric fluid produces muscular motions, if the whole animal machine is primarily operated by its action, it is clearly understandable why, in either excess or deficiency of electric powers, various differences of health should arise. But these things will be perceived by the more sagacious physicians, to whom they pertain.

XXIX. Galvani's theory seemed to produce some vicissitudes in Haller's[20] theory of irritability. For electricity, which to the Hallerians was merely an external stimulus, now becomes intrinsic in ourselves. For muscles constitute the most delicate electrometer of all, to which a moving cause is always attached by law and institution of nature. Therefore what the Hallerians assume by the term of irritability should be defined. For if they mean nothing else but a new phenomenon of nature, or property inherent in fibres, whereby elements approach one another, then there will be no conflict between the systems of Galvani and of Haller, but future correlation may be expected. For Galvani not only conceded that property to be inherent in muscular fibres, but considered it so necessary that, in its absence, wherever an arc was applied, you could not excite animal electricity. But if, by chance, to the Hallerians irritability is a new power inherent in fibres and producing muscular motions by itself alone, then surely one cannot acquiesce in their opinion, unless first they demonstrate the existence of irritability, and themselves prescribe definite laws, without which its true power cannot be understood: all which truly they are confident they can accomplish without difficulty, who demand the sole action of animal electricity. But already we have made sufficient statement about these things elsewhere.

XXX. But although, up to this time, very little exploration had been done, as to whether animal electricity should be regarded as a stimulant, or as the effective cause, of muscular motion, it was nevertheless always established that the mind, in making contrac-

[20] Albrecht von Haller, most eminent of Swiss anatomists, biologists, and physiologists; born at Bern, October 16, 1708, and died there December 17, 1777. He studied at Basel, Leyden, and Tübingen; was professor at Göttingen from 1736 to 1753; and practised in Bern from 1729 till his death. He was thrice married, and left eight children: he was also a philosopher and a poet.

tions, employs it as the handmaid of its authority, which surely had not been demonstrated before Galvani.

Sauvage and Bonnet,[21] illustrious men, had indeed suspected that electric fluid prepares muscular movements, chiefly because they had perceived that vigorous contractions are excited in muscles by artificial electricity. I remember also that in our Anatomical Theatre my uncle once and again so contended for the power of electric fluid in producing muscular motions that he seemed already, even at that time (as if he divined the outcome), to be striving for that in order that a hypothesis very dear to him might be converted into an approved thesis. But though all authorities granted their praise, there was no one, interested in physiological matters, who did not desire a more abundant confirmation of the truth. There were not lacking also those who applied all condemnations of hypotheses on electricity, perhaps not noting that other physiological opinions advanced were also hypotheses. Meanwhile, although at first nature offered difficulty to the sedulous investigator, yet when questioned more and more times, she responded to his wishes and diligence with unexpected cumulative reward of his antecedent labor. Finally bright day shone on Physiology and on Galvani, when he was able not only to produce and explain animal electricity, which he had formulated in his own mind, but to see it with his own eyes, handle it, and direct it where he wished.

XXXI. But when Galvani's *Commentary* had barely been published, an occasion of illustrating the theory of animal electricity presented itself most opportunely. For a studious youth, who had begun to be intensely fond of animal electricity, insistently demanded from Galvani that when, in accordance with his established plan, he had decided to demonstrate Neurology publicly, he should undertake in his lecture also to explain and illustrate the new system. Hence with a great multitude of auditors the physiological exercises were held, to which were added the experiments which illustrated the proposed part of the theory. Galvani never dissimulatingly avoided the accusations which had been made against ani-

---

[21] Charles Bonnet, eminent Swiss naturalist and philosopher, born at Geneva, March 13, 1720; died at Genthod, May 20, 1793. He studied law, and in 1743 became a LL.D. and a Fellow of the Royal Society. But he devoted his life to study of the natural sciences, and wrote many books in these disciplines. Of nerve fluid he writes: "The physiologists, who believe it analogous to the ether or to electric fluid, base their belief on facts and curious experiences, which all appear to testify in favor of the electric nature of nerve fluid."

mal electricity, but exposed them candidly in his public lecture, and estimated them with modest criticism, which was prompted not by disparagement of another's industry, but solely by love of truth. But I, since at that time I was most gratefully assisting my beloved uncle in the public performance of experiments in Physics, could not refrain from asking him, in my own name and that of the others, that, should an occasion again present itself of publishing his *Commentary*, he would himself amplify and enrich it with the more recently performed experiments and proposed conjectures. Since he could not undertake this, detained by other business, he consented that I should do it, and kindly communicated many data, which furnished the argument of added notes to the *Commentary*. Moreover, it was most acceptable both to gratify Galvani, to whom I owed most, and at the same time to look forward to augmentations of the theory of animal electricity.

XXXII. Finally, in the Fourth Part of his *Commentary*, in order that he might leave nothing untried, Galvani prepared muscular fibres and absolutely confirmed his hypothesis, both by its simplicity and by its felicity in explaining the more difficult phenomena of muscular motion. But what behoves them who profess to be lovers of truth, and really are, is that each should not arrogantly trust too much his own opinion, but be ready to relinquish it easily, if only he perceives another more probable. And this I mention, not merely because I think their counsel should be approved who, when they apply themselves to investigating the laws of animal electricity, if perchance they encounter any offense of obscurity, immediately condemn and reject, with a more severe precipitate judgment, everything which proves its certain existence. For if the repute and integrity of philosophic opinions were brought into conflict, when only a slight doubt is proposed, we should have very few or none of those theories which are the moderators and guides of human understanding. Wherefore they seem better to have provided for their name and fame and for the utility of physiology who judged that their minds should be not downcast by the empty fear of difficulties, but invited to glory by the sweetest reward of prospective praise. If the fear of contradiction had from the beginning deterred the illustrious men who first thought out the circulation of the blood, we should have lacked that noble discovery, and many things which are now clearly revealed in Physiology would still have lain in darkness.

Commentary Concerning the Effects of Electricity on Muscular Motion

by
Luigi Galvani

Concerning the Effects of Electricity
on Muscular Motion

In my desire to make that which, with no inconsiderable expenditure of pains, after many experiments, I have succeeded in discovering in nerves and muscles, so far useful that both their concealed properties might be revealed, if possible, and we might be able more surely to heal their diseases, nothing seemed more suitable for fulfilling such a wish than if I should simply publish my results, just as they are, for general judgment. For learned and eminent scholars, by reading my discoveries, will be able, through their own meditations and experiments, not only to amplify and extend them, but also to attain that which I indeed have attempted, but perhaps have not fully achieved.

It was also my desire not to publish this work in a crude and barely incipient form, even though not perfect and complete, which perhaps I should never have been able to do. But since I realized that I had neither time nor leisure nor ability sufficient to accomplish that, I preferred rather to fall short of my own very reasonable desire than to fail the practical value of the work.

I thought, therefore, that I should be doing something worth while, if I reported a brief and accurate account of my discoveries and findings in the order and relation in which partly chance and fortune presented and partly diligence and industry revealed them to me; not so much lest more be attributed to me than to fortune, or more to fortune than to me, but that either I might hand on a torch to those who had wished to enter this same pathway of experiment, or might satisfy the honest desire of scholars who are wont to be interested in things which contain some novelty either in origin itself or in principle.

But to the description of the experiments I will add some corollaries, and some conjectures and hypotheses, primarily with this purpose, that I may smooth the way for understanding new experiments, whereby, if we cannot attain the truth, at least a new approach thereto may be opened. The affair began at first as follows:

Part One

THE EFFECTS OF ARTIFICIAL ELECTRICITY ON MUSCULAR MOTION

I dissected and prepared a frog, as in Fig. 2, Tab. I, and placed it on a table, on which was an electrical machine, Fig. 1, Tab. I, widely removed from its conductor and separated by no brief interval. When by chance one of those who were assisting me gently touched the point of a scalpel to the medial crural nerves, DD, of this frog, immediately all the muscles of the limbs seemed to be so contracted that they appeared to have fallen into violent tonic convulsions. But another of the assistants, who was on hand when I did electrical experiments, seemed to observe that the same thing occurred whenever a spark was discharged from the conductor of the machine, (Fig. 1, B).

He, wondering at the novelty of the phenomenon, immediately apprised me of the same, wrapped in thought though I was and pondering something entirely different. Hereupon I was fired with incredible zeal and desire of having the same experience, and of bringing to light whatever might be concealed in the phenomenon. Therefore I myself also applied the point of a scalpel to one or other crural nerve at a time when one or other of those who were present elicited a spark. The phenomenon always occurred in the same manner: violent contraction in individual muscles of the limbs, just as if the prepared animal had been seized with tetanus, were induced at the same moment of time in which sparks were discharged.

But fearing lest these very motions arose rather from the contact of the point, which perchance acted as a stimulus, than from the spark, I again tested the same nerves in the same way in other frogs, and even more severely, but without any spark being elicited at that time by anyone; but no motions were seen at all. Hence it occurred to me that perhaps for the induction of the phenomenon both the contact of some body and the passage of a spark were simultaneously required. Wherefore I applied the edge of the scalpel again to the nerves and held it motionless, both at the time when a spark was being elicited and when the machine was perfectly quiet. But the phenomenon appeared only when the spark was produced.

We repeated the experiment, always employing the same scalpel: but not without our surprise, sometimes, when the spark was produced, the aforesaid motions occurred, sometimes they were lacking.

Aroused by the novelty of the circumstance, we resolved to test it in various ways, and to experiment, employing nevertheless the same scalpel, in order that, if possible, we might ascertain the causes of the unexpected difference; nor did this new labor prove vain; for we found that the whole thing was to be attributed to the different part of the scalpel by which we held it with our fingers: for since the scalpel had a bone handle, when the same handle was held by the hand, even though a spark was produced, no movements resulted, but they did ensue, if the fingers touched either the metallic blade or the iron nails securing the blade of the scalpel.

Now, since dry bones possess a non-conductile, but the metallic blade and the iron nails a conductile nature, we came into this suspicion, that perhaps it happened that when we held the bony handle with our fingers, then all access was cut off from the electric current, in whatever way it was acting on the frog, but that it was afforded when we touched the blade or the nails communicating therewith.

Therefore, to place the matter beyond all doubt, instead of a scalpel we used sometimes a slender glass cylinder H, Fig. 2, wiped clean from all moisture and dust, and sometimes an iron cylinder G. With the glass cylinder we not merely touched but rubbed the crural nerves, when the spark was elicited, but with all our effort, the phenomenon never appeared, though innumerable and violent sparks were elicited from the conductor of the machine, and at a short distance from the animal; but it appeared when the iron cylinder was even lightly applied to the same nerves and scanty sparks elicited.

Hence it appeared to us clearly established, what we had suspected to be true, that contact of a conducting body with the nerves is also required in order that the phenomenon should occur. But when both the body by which the nerves were touched, and the man who touched them, could be available, we applied the iron cylinder G to the same nerves, without touching it with our hands, that by this means it might be determined whether the phenomenon was to be ascribed to the man and the iron cylinder, or to the latter alone. When things were thus disposed, no motion of the muscles occurred when a spark was produced. Therefore, in place of the cylinder, we employed a very long wire, KK, to see whether in any way that

TABLE I

would replace the lack of the man, or not; and again there were contractions of the muscles on the passage of the spark.

From these observations it was clear to us that there is required not only the application of a conducting body to the nerves, but also a certain magnitude and extension thereof, for the production of the phenomenon. Hereafter, for the sake of perspicuity, not of brevity, let us be permitted to call such a conductor a nerve-conductor.

Moreover, we attached to the extremity of this conductor a frog by means of a small hook fixed into its spinal cord, Fig. 2, and sometimes placed the frog opposite the machine, sometimes placed its conductor so that the frog was now near the machine, now far distant from it, and therefore now the feet, now the prepared nerves, were turned towards the machine, which had the conductor now before now behind it; nevertheless contractions were always obtained equally.

We investigated moreover whether the phenomenon would be obtained in prepared animals, from a machine situated far distant, and this employing very long nerve-conductors. Moreover, the trial was so conducted that when an iron wire, 150 feet long and more, was employed, nevertheless, when a spark was produced, contractions of the muscles occurred, even at so great a distance from the machine.

We arranged an experiment in this way. We suspended an iron wire, EEE, Fig. 3, by a series of silk threads and, as the physicists say, insulated it. One end we attached similarly by silk threads to a nail driven in the wall, F; the other we conducted far from the machine the length of the wire into various other rooms. To this, at point C, we attached another iron wire, B, to whose extremity a frog was attached; and for convenience enclosed the frog in a glass jar, A, the bottom of which was filled with some conducting material, like water, for example, or very fine lead shot, whereby a better experiment resulted. But when a spark was produced from the conductor of the machine, surprisingly the headless frog moved at so great a distance and jumped vigorously about. The same thing happened if a frog outside the glass jar was attached in the same way to conductor EE, and far more quickly if there were attached to its feet some conducting body which communicated with the earth.

Having ascertained the situation in an insulated conductor, we explored what would happen with one not insulated.

For this purpose, we attached the same iron wire to various hinges of doors of chambers of our house, which were six in number, other things having been prepared as before: smaller contractions, but some in a prepared frog, appeared, when a spark was elicited.

These observations having been made, I resolved to investigate also whether the effect of such electricity would act and diffuse itself in all directions and in a circle. Therefore, having distributed various nerve-conductors circularly around the conductor of the machine at no short distance therefrom, and having attached a prepared frog to every single one of them, and having produced a spark, at one and the same time, not infrequently, the individual frogs moved, especially when the conducting body, as in the previous experiment, was attached to the feet of individual frogs, and most strongly when it was extended as far as the ground which was easily accomplished, either by a long metal wire attached to the individual feet of frogs, or if the frogs were grasped with the fingers.

But when we discovered the use and necessity of conducting bodies attached to the feet, it filled us with the desire to undertake other experiments concerning this matter; and, when these had been performed, it was determined that conducting bodies attached to muscles, for the purpose of obtaining contractions, were either sometimes alone sufficient without nerve conductors, or at least certainly with no small influence thereon; and the more, the larger they were and the more they excelled in power of conduction; but most, if they communicated with the earth; but at least they were as powerful as those we were accustomed to attach to nerves.

These conductors we will hereafter call muscle-conductors, that they may be conveniently distinguished from those which we have called nerve-conductors.

Now, indeed, we saw no contractions ensue when a spark was produced, even when we attached its conductor to each of the muscles, if the nerve-conductor, extended far from the machine, were intercepted by any non-conducting body, as if it were carefully prepared partly from conductile metal substance, partly from non-conductile substance, like glass or resin or silk, as if the conductor B, Fig. 3 were not attached to conductor EE at point C, but were suspended in a silk sling D; a new and indubitable demonstration that electricity flows through such conductors.

But we tested the fact not only by interception but also by total interruption of the conductor, and with the extremities of the interrupted conductor placed at a minimal distance from one another: there was no manifestation of any phenomenon at all.

But we endeavored also in some other way to interrupt the free passage of electricity through the conductor. We placed a prepared animal on an insulated surface, but did not, as before, connect its nerve-conductor either with the nerves or with the spinal cord, but placed it on the same surface in such a way that its extremity was distant from them several lines, sometimes even an inch; contractions resulted when a spark was elicited, they occurred also in limbs on the conducting surface when the nerves were placed at the same distance on an insulated surface or held elevated between the fingers, whether a short or a long nerve-conductor were employed, and whether the animal were near to or far from the machine. But they were completely lacking if the nerves and their conductor, separated from them as above, lay on a conducting surface.

And we did not fail to investigate whether this, which might be electricity, freely pervading not the surface merely but the substance of the conductors, nevertheless would excite the contractions of which we have often spoken. Therefore we wholly covered and invested, except for its extremities, the iron wire which constituted the nerve conductor with an insulating material, namely common wax, or sealing wax, or pitch. But, when a spark was produced, contractions occurred, as in the free conductor.

Moreover, these individual facts having been investigated and confirmed by a long series of experiments, it was possible not only to ascribe the phenomenon of such contractions to electricity, but also to note the conditions and as it were certain laws by which it was governed.

Muscular contractions of this sort, then, seemed to us, within certain limits, to vary directly with the strength of the spark and of the animal and especially the extent of the nerve-conductors, but inversely with the distance from the conductor of the machine. Likewise these contractions generally appeared to us greater when the animal was placed on the same table as the machine and the table was covered with oily pigment, or when the animal, removed from the table, was laid on an insulating, rather than on a conducting, substance.

I have said that it had seemed to me that a direct proportion was preserved in the contractions, but only within certain limits. For when, for example, a certain extension of the nerve-conductor has been found which is sufficient to produce the effect, if you diminish this, the contractions are not diminished but fail; but if you increase it, the contractions grow stronger, but only until you reach a certain extension, beyond which, however much you extend the nerve-conductor, they increase barely or not at all: and the same can be said of other elements of the stated proportion.

But indeed, so great was the observed capacity of the spark derived from the conductor of the machine for exciting muscular movements, that it seemed to us that much greater contractions were promised from the electric flame which breaks out when the circuit is overloaded. But the thing turned out altogether differently; for not without our amazement, in the animal prepared in the usual manner no motions ensued.

But now, these experiments having been made in positive electricity, as they say, it seemed to remain for us to make similar tests also in negative. First, therefore, we insulated the electrical machine and its operator. He held in his hand an iron cylinder to which we approximated the frogs provided, as was necessary, with their conductors; the frogs were placed on a glass surface, in order that no neighboring bodies might give them any electricity. Then the operator of the machine, with the iron cylinder which we have mentioned, industriously elicited sparks from the neighboring objects: we then saw contractions occur in the prepared frogs, just as they occurred with sparks elicited from the conductor of the non-insulated machine.

Moreover, we tested negative electricity in another way, which was as follows. At a certain distance from the negative surface of a Leyden jar we placed the nerve-conductor C, Fig. 4; then we elicited sparks Fig. 5 from the charged surface, as the physicists say, or from that which was endued with positive electricity. The frogs moved in the same way as when positive electricity was employed; they moved also when the iron wire, which constituted the nerve conductor, was at some distance from the external surface of the jar, and when it was wholly enclosed in a long glass tube and the frog itself guarded in a glass jar, if the open end of this tube touched the aforesaid external surface of the jar. Moreover, the same contractions were obtained, whether the spark was elicited from the crook of the Leyden jar at the same time when the said jar, as they say,

was being charged, or in the same place in which it was charged, or
elsewhere, and far removed from the machine.

These phenomena, moreover, occurred when the frogs were
equipped not only with a nerve-conductor, but merely with a muscle-
conductor: in a word everything was confirmed in this experiment of
the jar, as in the former of the machine, if the prepared animal could
receive no electricity from the external surface of the jar, or from
neighboring bodies, or from any other possible source.

But we wished also in another way to test electric surfaces negatively, and by eliciting sparks from them, to investigate such contractions; therefore I placed a prepared frog on the upper surface of
the square to which the electricity of the machine was constantly
flowing, and elicited a spark from the inferior surface, both when the
machine was quiet and when it was rotating. Rarely, though sometimes, when it was quiet, but then only from quiet of the machine;
but never when rotating, did the customary contractions of the
muscles fail to occur.

These experiments having been made by means of the electric
machine, we also called to the experiment electricity of an electrophor, that we might omit no kind of electricity exhibiting a spark.
Therefore we elicited a spark from the shield of an electrophor, and
the customary phenomenon of muscular contractions presented itself, not at as great distances as when the spark was elicited from the
conductor of a machine, but at very short distances; moreover the
contractions themselves were very slight. Although, indeed, after so
many experiments, there seemed to us scarcely any doubt about the
effects of electricity, and scarcely any about the cause of the phenomenon, nevertheless nothing occurred to us more suitable for con-
firming the thing more and more than to apply the most delicate
electrometers to animal conductors.

To these, therefore, we adapted a small electrometer constructed
after the manner of the justly celebrated Volta, whose straws, that
they might be more suitable for the experiment we covered on one
side with very thin silver-foil: when the experiment was performed,
when the insulated conductors of the machine were in rotation, the
straws not infrequently were separated one from another, but they
often came together again on the passage of the spark; but when
they were free, not least in rotation of the machine, the straws mutually receded one from another, and on extortion of the spark pro-

duced little leaps and vibrations which seemed to indicate some passage of electricity through the conductors of the animal at the time when contractions are excited at the extortion of a spark.

Now indeed, that the thing might be put beyond all doubt, we have striven in various ways to cut off all access for electric fluid of the machine in any way acting both on the animal and on his conductors. First, therefore, I enclosed the animal in a glass jar, then in one with a perforated wall, near which was an electrical machine, and into this foramen, which pierced the entire thickness of the wall, I inserted a glass tube so that a nerve-conductor, passing through the inserted tube, so fitted the orifice of the jar, artificially closed with glue, that it passed from the opposite surface of the wall and hung down into the next room. When a spark was elicited from the conductor of the machine, muscular motions ensued.

Conversely also I placed the animal and his conductor, with the conductor in the jar where first the animal was, and the animal where first the conductor hung; then I placed everything in the same arrangement as before, and elicited a spark, and the same movements ensued.

But although by this kind of experiment every pathway for electric fluid of the machine seemed cut off, nevertheless I devised and constructed a little machine, Fig. 6, which was far simpler and more convenient than the apparatus hitherto described, and which could easily be placed at various distances from the (large) machine, and within which not only the animal, but also both the nerve-conductor and the muscle-conductor, could easily be enclosed and concealed.

Now the little machine is of this nature. It is composed of two glass jars, of which one rests upon the other. In the upper jar is the nerve-conductor, which, for the sake of convenience, can be made of small lead shot, which can serve as muscle-conductor, since the animal, standing in them with his feet, has them as it were attached to his muscles.

The animal in this situation both is easily restrained and has communication with the conductor of the superior jar through his spinal cord by means of an iron wire which both is attached to the cork stopper of the same jar, and projects in its cavity, and is surrounded and covered with lead shot.

One must beware of this kind of stopper, lest, when the upper jar is inverted, that it may be superimposed on the other, the lead

shot fall out; and lest the same jar easily become separated from the
lower, and the electric fluid find a way for itself through the cracks
which may easily remain between the mouths of both jars, their lips
are attached and stuck together by a certain special glue made of
wax and turpentine, firmly but nevertheless so that the jars can be
separated and joined again in accordance with desire and opportunity.

Now when this little machine is placed on the table on which is
the electric machine, at a certain distance from the conductor of the
same, and a spark is produced, movements are seen, not merely the
same but more vigorous than when the animal and his conductors
are exposed to the open air; and the laws, which were indicated
above for the muscular movements were maintained in the given
proportion. These things having been observed, I would readily
have forsaken my first opinion, whereby I considered the electricity
of the conductor of the machine, in whatever way or manner excited
in the extortion of the spark as the active origin and cause of these
muscular movements, unless I had been recalled to the same opinion
both by experiments previously performed and by a rising suspicion
that the phenomenon was chiefly to be ascribed to electricity of the
interior surface of the glass acting on the animal and its conductors
at the time of discharge of the spark; in which suspicion, indeed, I
was wholly confirmed not only by other experiments subsequently
instituted, but also in the first by the movements of the electrometer located in the same little machine. For the very light shot and
the wires, of which the electrometer was composed, changed position
immediately when the machine was turned, and were restored again,
when sparks were elicited, into their former position and contact.

Now, indeed, these and other things having been performed and
ascertained, that seemed at last to remain which promised the greatest usefulness in our experiments, that we should institute them also
in living animals.

This therefore we did with the crural nerve, not dissected inside
the abdomen, lest the animals might easily die, but exposed in the
thigh and separated from adjacent structures and drawn outside the
muscles, and the conductor applied to it; contractions ensued on the
passage of the spark in the corresponding leg alone, only less, as it
seemed to us, than in the dead animal.

But since in our individual experiments, hitherto described, the animal and the machines and conductor communicated one with another through the intervening atmosphere, we wished also to ascertain what would happen if this communication first were interrupted and then finally restored.

First I accomplished it as follows: arranged under a glass jar, as in Fig. 6, I placed a little machine along with a prepared animal and its conductors at a short distance from an electric machine; then I elicited a spark, and motions occurred according to custom.

I then placed this same jar, along with an enclosed little machine, under another much larger, and this under another still larger: again, when a spark was elicited, similar motions ensued, though feebler the greater the number of recipients and the thickness of their walls.

After this, I cut off all communication of air between the animal and the electric machine. Namely, I placed the little machine, in which was the animal, in the receiver of a pneumatic machine, in a place moderately distant from the conductor of an electric machine; I perforated the upper jar of the little machine, in order that the air might be evacuated from it by repeated exhaustions: then, sometimes when the air was exhausted, and sometimes when it was not, I elicited a spark: contractions occurred in each case, nor, as it seemed, were they appreciably dissimilar.

Now then, electricity acting through a spark having been tested in such various ways, we investigated with diligence and labor whether it exercised its control also by other effects and means on muscular motion. Sometimes it was possible to observe muscular contractions, if the nerve-conductor, B, Fig. 3, was placed as near as possible to the conductor of the electric machine, then the shield of the electrophore raised from the resinous surface, or if the same shield were transferred close to the same conductor, when the electrophore was far distant from the same conductor, without any spark being elicited.

These experiments were all performed in animals which are called cold-blooded. These things having been tested and discovered, nothing was more in my desires than to perform the same or similar experiments in warm-blooded animals, as for example in hens and in sheep. The experiment having been tried, the result was the same in the latter as in the former. But there was need of a different preparation in the latter; for it was necessary first to expose the crural nerve, not inside the abdomen, but externally in the thigh itself, and to separate it from other parts and bring it to the surface, then apply the conductor to it, and then elicit the spark from the conductor of the machine, with the leg either attached to the living animal or resected from it as soon as possible; for otherwise, if the customary manner of preparing frogs were employed, the phenomenon was wholly lacking, perhaps because the power of self-contraction of the muscles was lacking beforehand, which that long and complex preparation can release.

But indeed, in this kind of experiments, whether in warm or in cold animals, there are some things at the end, and these peculiar and, as I think, not unimportant to note, which never presented themselves to us. One was that prepared animals were more suitable for these phenomena, the more advanced they were in age, and also the whiter their muscles were and the more they were deficient in blood, and therefore perhaps the muscular contractions were prompter and easier and could be excited much longer in cold than in warm animals; for the former, in comparison with the latter, have more dilute blood, more difficult to coagulate, and therefore flowing much more easily from the muscles: another was that prepared animals, in whom these electric experiments were undertaken, decay and rot much more quickly than those who have suffered no electric force: finally that even if the phenomena which we have described thus far as occurring did so in the way we stated, animals prepared for experiment fail differently. For if the conductors are applied not to the dissected spinal cord or to the nerves, as we have been accustomed, but are applied or even attached to the brain or the muscles, or if nerve conductors are extended or prolonged, or if nerves according to custom are in the least detached from surrounding parts, the contractions are either none or very slight. Many accepted things certainly, which we have discovered from these experiments, we refer chiefly to this method of preparing and separating nerves.

Part Two

THE EFFECTS OF ATMOSPHERIC ELECTRICITY
ON MUSCULAR MOTION

Having discovered the effects of artificial electricity on muscular contractions which we have thus far explained, there was nothing we would sooner do than to investigate whether atmospheric electricity, as it is called, would afford the same phenomena, or not: whether, for example, by employing the same devices, the passage of lightning, as of sparks, would excite muscular contractions.

Therefore we erected, in the fresh air, in a lofty part of the house, a long and suitable conductor, namely an iron wire, and insulated it, Fig. 7, and to it, when a storm arose in the sky, attached by their nerves either prepared frogs, or prepared legs of warm animals, as in Fig. 20, 21, Tab. IV. Also we attached another conductor, namely another iron wire, to the feet of the same, and this as long as possible, that it might extend as far as the waters of the well indicated in the figure. Moreover, the thing went according to our desire, just as in artificial electricity; for as often as the lightning broke out, at the same moment of time all the muscles fell into violent and multiple contractions, so that, just as the splendor and flash of the lightning are wont, so the muscular motions and contractions of those animals preceded the thunders, and, as it were, warned of them; nay, indeed, so great was the concurrence of the phenomena that the contractions occurred both when no muscle conductor was also added, and when the nerve conductor was not insulated, nay it was even possible to observe them beyond hope and expectation when the conductor was placed on lower ground, Fig. 8, particularly if the lightnings either were very great, or burst from clouds nearer the place of experimentation, or if anyone held the iron wire F in his hands at the same time when the thunderbolts fell.

Moreover, the phenomenon occurred whether the animal was exposed in the fresh air, or, for the sake of convenience, had been enclosed in a suitable jar, as in Fig. 7, or kept within the room. It occurred also although the nerve-conductor was at some distance from the nerves themselves, particularly with lightnings either more violent or nearer, as we said occurred in artificial electricity when

36

the sparks were either stronger or extorted nearer the animal. Finally that worthy of notice occurred, that not merely by one contraction of muscles was the whole thing manifested in the lightning as in the spark, but by many, succeeding one another as it were in one mutual moment of time, of which the number of thunders seemed to correspond to the number which a thunderbolt is wont to produce.

Now, indeed, such contractions were produced not merely with lightning but in a stormy sky, with clouds passing over the almost removed conductors they arose for the most part spontaneously; and when this had happened, both the electrometers gave no slight signs of electricity, and not rarely sparks could be elicited from the conductors raised high in air, differently from when contractions were obtained with lightning-flashes; for then more often no sparks were elicited, and more delicate electrometers hardly aroused any suspicion of electricity.

Now experiments of this kind were undertaken not only in dead but also in living animals, and in both the phenomenon appeared, and none of those things was omitted which we have discovered in artificial electricity, but all for the most part occurred in the same way. At first sight, indeed, it seemed that this considerable difference existed, that the prepared frogs which, with a suitable conductor, were enclosed in a little glass machine, Fig. 6, Tab. I, separated from the conductor of the electric machine by an interval, on the passage of the spark were violently disturbed, as we said, but, when lightning burst from the clouds, were wholly quiescent; perhaps either because, if any electricity were conveyed from the electric cloud to the little machine by means of the conductor, it was very slight, and occupied a very small part of its surface, so that it was not adequate for inducing contractions, or perhaps because none was carried to the same little machine; just as for the most part, for the same reason the same contractions are lacking on the passage of the spark, if the little machine is placed, not near the electric machine, but near that end of the electric conductor, EE Fig. 3, Tab. I, which is far distant from the same machine.

Upon diligent investigation of the circumstance, on this account, the manner of action appears similar between artificial and atmospheric electricity; perhaps for obtaining these contractions within the little glass machine, it is necessary that the electric atmosphere, either wholly or for the most part, should surround the same ma-

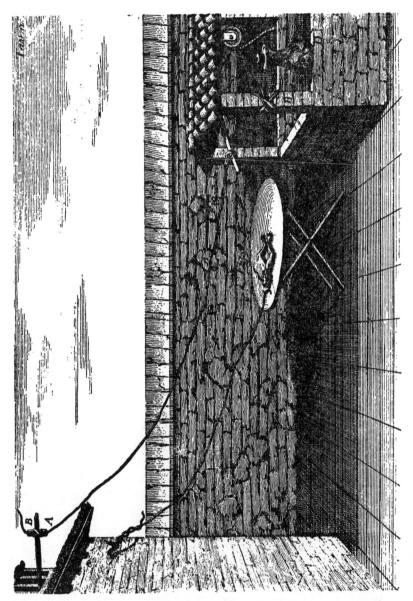

chine; but, from what has hitherto been stated, it seems to be far removed from the position of the little machine and from the experiment.

But not merely the phenomenon having been explored, but its laws also having been subjected to examination, we have ascertained that the same are maintained in no dissimilar manner in atmospheric, as are maintained in artificial, electricity.

Now, indeed, the effects of storm electricity, as they say, having been investigated, not of thunder and lighting alone, it occurred to us also to test what sheet lightning and northern lights would produce in animals prepared in the customary way. Therefore we adapted our animals to an atmospheric conductor not only during lightning but during northern lights. But no contractions were ever then produced, perhaps because either such coruscations do not depend on electricity or, if they do, either in too remote a place, or they occur for some very different reason than thunderbolts. But these are questions for the physicists.

Part Three

THE EFFECTS OF ANIMAL ELECTRICITY ON MUSCULAR MOTION

The effects of stormy atmospheric electricity having been tested, my heart burned with desire to test also the power of peaceful, everyday electricity.

Wherefore, since I had sometimes seen prepared frogs placed in iron gratings which surrounded a certain hanging garden of my house, equipped also with bronze hooks in their spinal cord, fall into the customary contractions, not only when the sky was lighting, but also sometimes when it was quiet and serene, I thought these contractions derived their origin from the changes which sometimes occur in atmospheric electricity. Hence, not without hope, I began diligently to investigate the effects of these changes on these muscular motions in various ways. Wherefore at different hours, and for many days, I inspected animals, appropriately adjusted therefor; but there was scarcely any motion in their muscles. Finally, weary with vain expectation I began to press the bronze hooks, whereby their spinal cords were fixed, against the iron gratings, to see whether by this kind of device they excited muscular contractions, and in various states of the atmosphere, and of electricity whatever variety and mutation they presented; not infrequently, indeed, I observed contractions, but bearing no relation to varied state of atmosphere or of electricity.

Nevertheless, since I had not inspected these contractions except in the fresh air, for I had not yet experimented in other places, I was on the point of seeking such contractions from electricity of the atmosphere, which had crept into the animal and accumulated in him and gone out rapidly from him in contact of the hook with the iron grating; for it is easy in experimentation to be deceived, and to think one has seen and discovered what we desire to see and discover.

But when I had transported the animal into a closed chamber and placed him on an iron surface, and had begun to press against it the hook fixed in his spinal cord, behold the same contractions and the same motions! Likewise continuously, I tried using other metals, in other places, other hours and days; and the same result; except that the contractions were different in accordance with the diversity of metals, namely more violent in some, and more sluggish in others. Then it continually occurred to me to employ for the same experiment other bodies, but those which transmit little or no electricity, glass for example, gum, resin, stone, wood, and those which are dry; nothing similar occurred, it was not possible to observe any muscular motions or contractions. Results of this sort both brought us no slight amazement and began to arouse some suspicion about inherent animal electricity itself. Moreover both were increased by the circuit of very thin nervous fluid which by chance we observed to be produced from the nerves to the muscles, when the phenomenon occurred, and which resembled the electric circuit which is discharged in the Leyden jar.

For, while I myself held in one hand a prepared frog on a hook fixed in his spinal cord, and manipulated him so that with his feet he rested on a silver box, with the other hand I touched with some metal object the surface of the same box on which the frog rested with his feet, or his sides, and beyond expectation I saw the frog fall into no slight contractions, and indeed as often as I employed the same kind of device.

Having made these observations I asked Rialpus, a Spaniard, a very learned man, formerly a Fellow of the Society of Jesus, who was then rusticating with me in the villa of the most excellent and noble gentleman, Jacob Zambeccari, I asked him, I say, that as in other experiments he was very kindly accustomed, so in this he would afford me a helpful and assisting hand and hold the frog, as I myself did formerly, while I myself touched the box again, both for convenience and in order that I might change a little my mode of experimentation. But, contrary to expectation, the contractions failed; I continued the experiment as before, and performed it alone; and immediately they returned.

This moved me to hold the animal myself with one hand, as before, and with the other the hand of Rialpus and to ask him that he himself with his other hand should either touch or strike the box in which the appearance of an electric circuit was produced: immediately the same phenomenon of the contractions occurred, not without our pleasure and wonder, because it was again lacking, if we removed our hand, and appeared again if the hand were replaced.

TABLE III

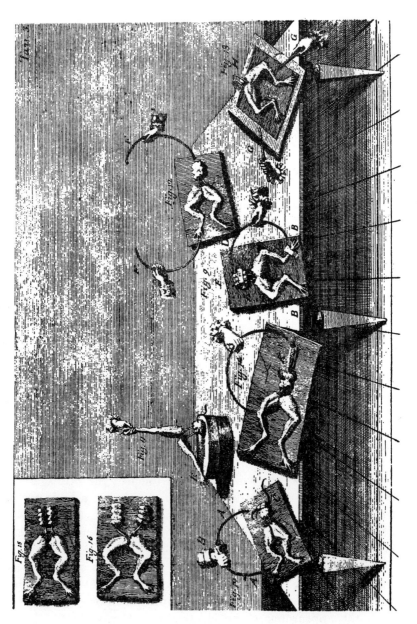

But although it seemed that these things could all be demonstrated as an electric extension of the nerve fluid through the human chain, nevertheless, in order that we might more and more confirm a thing so great and concealing so much novelty, we wished that not by the clasp of hands alone but through some intermediate body, either insulating, like a glass cylinder, or conducting, like a metal cylinder, Rialpus and I should constitute the chain; but, the experiment having been made, we beheld, not without pleasure, that the phenomenon occurred when a metal cylinder was employed, but failed altogether when glass was employed or when it was touched in vain or when the box was struck with heavier blows of the conducting body; so that on this account we considered it as ascertained that electricity of this sort excites contractions, in whatever way it may ultimately do this.

But, in order that I might put the thing more in the open, it was most opportune for me to place the frog on an insulating surface, namely glass or resin; then to employ either the whole arc or the conducting arc or in part the non-conducting arc, one end of it with a hook fixed to the spine; the other end applied either to the muscles of the leg or to the feet. But when the experiment had been done, we saw the contractions performed when the conducting arc was employed, Fig. 9, but fail completely when we used the arc partly conducting and partly insulating, as in Fig. 10. The conducting arc was of iron wire, but the hook of brass wire.

These things having been observed, it seemed to us that the contractions which we have said occurred in frogs placed on a metal surface when a hook in the spinal cord was pressed towards the same plane, ought to be repeated by a similar arc whose ends should be borne in some way by a metallic plane, and hence it should result that contractions should not be excited in frogs placed on any insulating surface, provided the same devices were employed altogether.

This opinion of ours, if I judge correctly, was clearly confirmed by a not inopportune phenomenon casually observed: for if a frog is held in the fingers so suspended by one leg that a hook fixed in the spinal cord touches a silver surface and the other leg freely falls into the same plane, Fig. 11, Tab. III, as soon as this same leg touches the surface itself immediately the muscles contract, wherefore the the leg rises and is drawn up, but soon relaxes of its own accord and again falls to the surface, and as soon as it comes in contact with it, is again elevated for the same reason, and so it continues thereafter to rise and fall alternately, so that, like an electric pendulum, the same leg seems to imitate the other, not without admiration and pleasure on the part of the beholder.

It is easy to see how conveniently and aptly this phenomenon can be repeated, taking turns on the supporting surface with each arc most fit for the aforesaid circuit, while it calls the free leg to the same surface, but to the circuit wholly different, at the same time that the other leg recedes from it. These are neither doubtful nor obscure signs of the metallic surface bearing alternate arcs.

But it can hardly be said what is the capacity and aptitude of this surface for exciting muscular contractions, that namely whereby contractions may be obtained, both great and frequent, sometimes even constant for a long time, not only if the hook fixed in the spinal cord is either pressed against the metallic surface itself, or rubbed against it, but also at the same time that the hook itself touches the same surface, and if it afterwards touches it, some of its contacts with the surface are changed, as if you lightly strike either the surface on which the animal is, or the bodies on which the same plane rests. But concerning the kind of arc which the metallic plane carries, so much for the present.

But before our discussion leaves the use and capacities of the arc, we do not wish to omit this about its capacity and I almost said necessity for demonstrating this kind of muscular contractions as conveniently as possible, that the same are obtained, and often, more clearly and promptly not merely with one but with two arcs also, disposed and employed in such a way that one extremity of one arc is applied to muscles, one extremity of the other arc to nerves, and the two remaining extremities are brought to mutual contact, or if necessary are touched alternately, Fig. 12. In which this peculiarity is observed: that electricity of this sort, incuding contractions, is not to any appreciable degree diffused or dissipated either by contact of the hands with either arc or by repeated contacts of the arcs with parts of the animal.

But that is also peculiar and worthy of notice when the strength, particularly of prepared animals, languishes, around the arc-conductors or conducting surfaces, it befell us very often to observe that various and multiple metal substances are very effective both for obtaining and for increasing muscular contractions, and indeed far more than one and the same metallic substance. So, for example, if the whole arc were iron, or the hook iron and the conducting surface likewise iron, very often the contractions will either fail or will be very scanty. But if one of them were iron, for example, and the other bronze, much more if it were silver (for silver, in comparison with other metals, seems to us preferable for conducting animal electricity), contractions will occur continuously and far greater and far longer. The same thing happens when one surface of an insulating plane is separated in two places, and equally covered with dissimilar metal foil, as for example, if, in one place, you employ tinfoil, in another, brass-foil, contractions will occur as much greater as possible than if each place were covered, or, as they say, armatured, with one and the same metal, even silver-foil.

But, indeed, this sort of a circuit of nervous fluid, like electric fire, having been detected, this seemed the twofold consequence, that both this or a dissimilar, or rather contrary electricity produces this phenomenon, as it were duplex, either in a Leyden jar or that electricity in the charged arc through which it discharges its electric fluid like a circle; for the movement of electricity cannot be held as a circuit by the demonstrating physicists, except in restoration of equilibrium, and either solely or chiefly between contrary electricities. Moreover, in one and the same metal there lay concealed those opposite by nature which seemed contrary to observations: therefore it remained that each resided in the animal. Nor did I have any suspicion in experimenting that any kind of electricity could have been ascribed to animals, I attached the bronze arc covered with silver leaf to the glass cylinder, which I held in my hands, when I applied the arc itself to animals; when this precaution was employed, contractions nevertheless occurred.

These experiments having been performed in the fresh air, the thought entered my mind, what would happen to the electricity of an animal, if I should submerge the animal himself under water: this therefore I did, and according to custom applied to him the extremities of an arc, one with an iron hook to the spinal cord, the other to the feet: contractions occurred just as in the fresh air.

But this peculiarity presented itself to me in this experiment, that if either with the same arc or with any other conducting body I merely touched the hook in the spinal cord of the animal lying under the water, immediately contractions occurred; which I myself referred to the water transmitting the arc in turn. Therefore I immersed the animal not in water as before, but in oil, to see whether contractions occurred just as under water, or were wholly lacking. Then I applied the same conducting body to the hook in the spinal cord as before; the contractions wholly failed, the oil being wholly unequal to taking turns with the conducting arc, a thing which confirmed me not a little in my preconceived opinion.

These things having been ascertained and noted, it seemed to me that I could best proceed without any delay to find that double and opposite electricity in the prepared animal itself, and that either one has its location in muscle, the other in nerve, or both in either, as the physicists affirm in the Tourmaline Stone. With all zeal, therefore, I began to seek and investigate this location; and first what kind of electricity nerves present. Therefore to the spinal cord of one of the headless frogs, which I had recently prepared in as large number as possible, having been killed for experiment, I closely applied a cylinder, now glass, now made of sealing-wax; but never at first application did muscular movements occur; but they were observed when another was employed, generally at a distance of four or more lines, provided the vertebral tube and had been covered with tin-foil, as we shall say below. In place of the glass cylinder, we often used the disc of the electric machine, driven by numerous revolutions, in order that we might ascertain whether the greater supply of electricity which was collected in the disc would excite those muscular contractions which the cylinder could not, but the experiment had the same result; not the slightest motions occurred in the muscles.

Therefore the nerve-electricity in the experiments will be positive since the physicists demonstrate that only between opposite electricities can known effects and motions be obtained.

Then we turned our mind to investigating the electricity of muscles: therefore we undertook the same experiments in these as in the former; but it was not possible to observe any movements in the muscles when either positive or negative electricity was employed.

Therefore we returned again to nerve-electricity, which was conforming to our experiments; and in exploring the same with sealing-wax we used the same devices, whereby we were burned while we tested it with the extortion of a spark. Nearly the same phenomena of contractions appeared, except that those were much less which were produced with sealing-wax, than those with a spark, corresponding to the strength of the electricity. The utility of the conductors was the same also, and their laws the same, and clearly the muscular motions appeared in the same way.

But since nothing seemed to be more suitable for discovering so obscure and difficult a thing, namely the location of each electricity, than to increase and apply the electricity, I therefore began to meditate sedulously concerning the method of accomplishing this, and, following analogy, this method presented itself first, that I should cover the nerves in which electricity seemed to prevail, and whose nature we had ascertained, with some metal foil, preferably of tin, no less than the physicists are accustomed to accomplish in their magic square and Leyden jar, Fig. 9, Tab. III.

With a device of this sort, it is amazing how much stronger muscular contractions grow, so much, indeed, that even without an arc, but with a single contact of a body of any nature, either conducting or even non-conducting, with armatured nerves, contractions appeared, provided only that they had been recently prepared and that their strength was maintained; so that the arc, and the strength and utility of other devices, proved far greater; that finally contractions became more violent and longer and fairly constant in animals vigorous before section, even if either the arc is removed or the body whereby the armatured nerves are touched.

What more? Such was the power and capacity of this device in increasing and augmenting the strength of this kind of electricity, that a circuit which barely, and not even barely, appeared when hooks and an arc were employed, emerged happily and promptly in a tadpole, not only through two men, but even sometimes through three and more, constituting, as it were, an electric chain, and muscular contractions were excited, especially in summer time, in older animals with pale muscles, and when a storm threatens in heaven. Moreover, in prepared animals, if the denuded cerebrum and denuded spinal cord are covered in some part with the same metal foil, when the arc was employed according to custom, contractions both vigorous and prompt then began to appear, which, however, without this kind of device, I had previously striven in vain to excite with the arc or in any other way.

Moreover, the effect of tin-foil applied to nerves having been found so great in augmenting animal electricity, I decided to try also what the same foil would do in muscles; but contractions were not seen to assume much increase, nay even, when the thing was tested more often, we finally noticed this, that some increase of contractions occurred if only with these parts, the muscles also were covered with the same layer of tin, and the arc applied to the armatured places.

Not only were the contractions extended by metal foil applied to the denuded spinal cord, but also by having the vertebral column covered with the same, applied not only externally in the back to its muscles, but internally in the abdomen, and especially in the region where the nerves emerge. And it did not matter if at first you had covered those parts and the nerves with much foil or with little, for it was sufficient if you should cover it with any, and should apply one extremity of the arc to it and the other to the muscles. But in place of the metal foil we employed with equal utility an electric amalgam, or sprinkled the nerve with its powder, or applied to the nerve a pastille made of the same powder with oil. But if we used any other metallic powder, iron, for example, or brass, even in the same way, there was scarcely any increase of muscular motions.

Now, indeed, having found the reason why this sort of electricity assumed so much increase, we then sought its location with more eagerness and confidence. Hence now a nerve, now a muscle being covered with the same foil, we drew out from the animal first the muscle with the corresponding nerve and placed it on an insulating surface, and applied an arc to it according to custom; we likewise did the same both in an intact muscle, and in a divided muscle, namely we enclosed one part of it in metal foil, then applied one extremity of an arc to the armatured part of the muscle, the other extremity to the bare muscle; but barely, and not even barely, were we permitted by these attempts to arrive at any of those things which we were seeking.

This only we noticed: in the muscle with its nerve brought outside the animal, far fewer contractions took place than if they had remained in their natural positions; moreover, in the intact muscle, though they were scanty hitherto, that they became much slighter, nay, hardly occurred at all; but nevertheless not rarely some, if one extremity of an arc were applied to an armatured place on a muscle, the other to an adjacent and bare surface of the same muscle; but

when the experiment was tried otherwise, none occurred: also that
it likewise happened, but with much more difficulty, in the internal
substance of a muscle; but that contractions arise far more easily and
promptly if the arc were applied in the same way to an armatured
nerve; nay, if the small extremity of an arc, in place of any other
conducting body, were called into use, and partly an edge of metal
foil and partly a bare nerve were touched by it.

These tests we made concerning the investigated location of animal electricity, by which it is established that the fact, which could
not be sufficiently illustrated by experiments, must be largely com-
mitted to conjecture.

Now let us pursue some matters which, as we diligently investigated this kind of electricity, presented themselves to us as worthy
of attention; among which this was foremost: that that excited by
common electricity always acts, as we have warned, at a distance of
several lines, but by itself alone not even at the shortest distance,
but always requires actual contact in order that it may exercise its
effect. But we see that greater contractions can often be obtained
more certainly and promptly, if the extremity of the arc is applied
to the very edge of a metallic layer covering nerves or muscles, than
if to the flat surface thereof; likewise if to the extremity of a hook
than if to the other parts thereof: whereby it appears that animal
electricity does not exactly imitate common, ordinary electricity,
whose peculiar nature it is to choose and follow angles and points.

These facts, so obvious and clear, to my judgment, about electricity in muscles and nerves, gave us additional courage that we
should more studiously investigate more and more data about the
same. Hence first, in place of the aforesaid metal foil, we covered
both nerves and muscles in some part with insulating material,
namely silk-web, oil in which pitch was dissolved and wholly imbued, to see whether contractions would be wholly lacking, when
the arc was employed, or not: they failed completely. But it was
necessary to employ the silk web, and to prepare it in such a way
that it was adequate to insulate contractions, because easily, in the
conducting animals, it became imbued and moistened with lymph,
and not oil alone, because it so yielded place to the extremity of the
arc that it came into altogether absolute contact with the under-
lying part.

Then we investigated whether this kind of electricity followed the theory and nature of common electricity in this, that it made itself an easier way through certain conducting bodies, and through others a more difficult one.

But we see it follows almost exactly; and first, as the former, so the latter makes its way more happily through metals than through wood, but among metals most happily through gold and silver, more feebly through lead and iron, particularly if the latter is corroded with rust, so that if either an arc, or surfaces substituting for an arc, were plated, and particularly with silver, or, which is more convenient, covered with very thin silver-foil, the phenomena of contractions would appear both far more clearly and far more promptly than if the same had been constructed either of lead, for example, or even of iron.

But having investigated the power of conduction in solid bodies, we also explored the same in fluids, and the thing came out the same way; namely we found that this kind of electricity makes its way very readily through aqueous fluids, but is wholly blocked and retarded by oily fluids. In order that we might investigate this, we used small glass tubes, which we closed at one end with some material through which we passed a metal wire, namely silver or brass, and passed it so covered with tin-foil that by one part it would be free inside the cavity of the tube, and by the other would be prolonged far from it; but the tubes we filled with material suitable for the experiment, namely sometimes aqueous, sometimes oily, and by a similar device closed them at the other extremity, and equipped them in the same way with a similar metallic wire. Things being thus arranged, we used tubes of this sort so that they constituted either a whole arc, by bending the metallic wires, or part of an arc whose extremities, according to custom, were applied to an animal. When these tubes were employed, Fig. 14 Tab. III, no contractions occurred when they had been filled with oil, but only when they had been filled with water.

Now, nothing seemed to conduce more to deriving utility from these experiments than to investigate diligently also the faculty of insulation or of conduction in different parts of animals. The experiment having been made we have ascertained that all parts of dissected animals freely conduct and transmit conveniently this kind of electricity, perhaps on account of the moisture by which they are washed, either by nature or in sections and preparations;

for if various and recently dissected parts, such as muscle fibers, cartilages, nerves, bones, membranes; or fluids, as blood, lymph, serum, urine, received on a glass plate, or enclosed in the aforesaid tubes, are applied to preparations, and especially to armatured nerves, and then to the same parts one end of an arc is adjusted, and muscles are touched by the other, then contractions as surely occur as if the same arc-end had been applied to the nerves themselves. Moreover, we ascertained that the same thing happens if things are arranged as it were in the opposite way, and the experiment undertaken with the aforesaid parts, not nerves but muscles being fitted, but with one extremity of the arc adjusted to the same parts, and the other to the armatured nerves. But we see the thing is otherwise, particularly if those solid parts have not recently been dissected, but are dry by nature or by art. And indeed the phenomenon does not appear solely in those parts artificially arranged, but also in the same either located hitherto by nature in the animal, or by reason certainly deviating little from the natural; for if one extremity of an arc is applied to insulated nerves, particularly armatured, and the other touches any other part of the body, intactly and naturally constituted, which ultimately responds to muscles supplied by the same nerves, the phenomenon almost always occurs, just as if the same extremity of the arc were applied to the muscles themselves; but not without some surprise we saw the same thing occur, both with nerves and with muscles first cut and separated from the circuit, then joined again in some artificial way. For if frogs are prepared in the customary way, and their vertebral column covered with tin-foil and their limbs divided with a knife so that each limb remains joined only to its own corresponding nerve, and then one limb removed far from the other, Fig. 15, Tab. III, then one extremity of an arc applied to the same vertebral column, the other to muscles, or only to the foot of one leg, then only the muscles of the same leg will move and contract.

But if the same limbs are carefully joined again so that they come into mutual contact, and the arc applied in the same way and to the same leg, then all the muscles of each leg will move and contract. Moreover exactly the same thing happens when the vertebral column is split, with the spinal cord along its axis, and then the parts of the divided column spread apart with their corresponding nerves, but the limbs joined as they are by nature; the muscles of only one limb fall into contractions when one extremity of an arc is applied to only one of the aforesaid parts of the vertebral column, the other to the corresponding leg; but the muscles of each leg fall into contractions when the parts of the divided spinal cord are again joined artificially, and the arc applied by one of its extremities to either limb, and the other to the same conjoined parts: finally exactly the same phenomena occur either with the intact trunk of a prepared animal, or with the trunk divided through the middle sagitally from top to bottom, provided the divided parts are artificially and carefully joined and brought into mutual contact, Fig. 16, Tab. III.

It does not seem that these phenomena can be sufficiently fitly explained except by the interposed moisture of the parts affording access and passage to the outflowing animal electricity. Will they be able to throw any light on the hitherto obscure cause and reason for the coöperation of nerves? Would that wiser physiologists would investigate this sometime! But perhaps nothing is more suitable for demonstrating powers of coöperation than if the crural nerves are prepared according to custom, and the spinal cord and head remain intact, and the upper limbs intact in nature and position.

For then, if either the crural nerve or the vertebral column is armatured, and the arc applied partly to the armatured part of the crural nerve and partly to the corresponding limb, not only the lower limbs contract, but the upper ones move also, the eyelids move, and other parts of the head move, so that on this account, the electric fluid, aroused by nervous contact of the arc, for the most part flows from the indicated place of the nerves to the muscles, but partly also through the nerves seeks the higher regions and is carried as far as the brain, and seems to carry such effect into it that thence, for whatever reason, motions of other muscles are excited.

But truly, although it would hardly seem permissible to doubt about animal electricity, confirmed both by experiments and by factors of analogy and reason, or about its presence and motion in nerves and in muscles, or about its exit either from the former, or from the latter, or from both, and about its free excursion through applied conducting bodies; and although we realize that fortune and industry have granted us no small fruit of our experiments, in that to us first perhaps they have revealed whereby to place the said electricity clearly before the eyes and to derive it from the animal and, as it were, to handle it with our hands; nevertheless, to confess the truth, the thing is not yet completely demonstrated and absolute in all respects, nor does it seem to us to have passed sufficiently out of the realm of opinion, unless we might be permitted also to ascertain the mode and reason, way and manner, whereby the same phenomena of contractions might be obtained without either nerves or muscles being touched in any way or by any substance.

We feared lest perhaps these phenomena might in some way be ascribed to some mechanical irritation either of the arc or other instruments, and that therefore it was not sufficiently established by these experiments themselves concerning the very tenuous electric fluid flowing out through nerves and inducing muscular contractions. Moreover, it occurred to me to try whether, with the nerves attached to one surface of the magic square, as the upper for example, and the muscles to the lower, Fig. 20, or the opposite, as in Fig. 13, and with one extremity of the arc applied to the former, the other to the latter, surface, in a place far removed from the displaced parts of the animal, contractions would occur or not. For by this sort of experiment I easily learned whether the fluid flowing out along the nerves had been electrical and the contractions had originated and started from its passage from the nerves to the muscles, whether it was the same as if I had applied the arc to muscles and nerves without its being possible for any suspicion to arise about mechanical stimulus being applied to them. But, the experiment having been made, we saw, not without some delight, that contractions occurred, without occurring by the same method, if glass or resinous surfaces armatured after the fashion of the physicists had been placed in one and the same plane, provided they had been separated by some distance from one another, so that the nerves were in one of those surfaces, the muscles in the other, and there had been no communication between them through an intermediate conducting body, Fig. 18. Moreover we observed that by this device contractions occurred without either nerves or muscles having been covered with metal foil in the customary method; and we finally noticed that they occurred if, for example, the spinal cord or the nerves were placed under water in one jar, the feet in another, and then, according to custom, the arc applied by its extremities to both surfaces of water, Fig. 19.

This moreover, furnished us occasion to investigate what would

TABLE IV

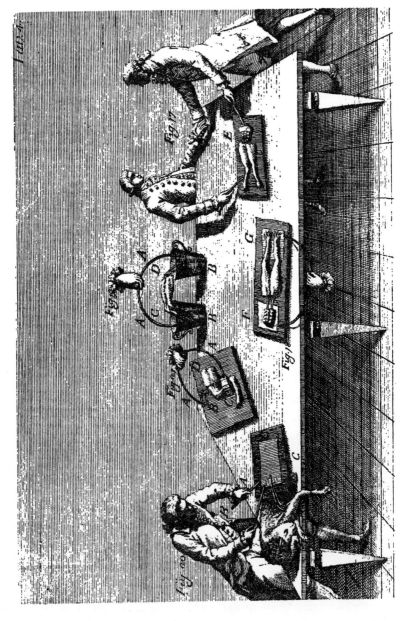

happen, if the muscles were placed on an armatured glass surface, the spinal cord in its own tube and joined to its nerves on a conducting surface, either connected by a hook or else armatured according to custom; what then would happen, if the experiment were otherwise arranged, namely with the spinal cord placed on the glass plate, conducting to the muscles, and the arc, as in the preceding experiment, applied to two opposite places, of which one should look towards the spinal cord, the other towards the muscles; what, finally, if both the cord and the muscles should be laid out on one and the same armatured surface. Truly the contractions were more languid, and were excited with more difficulty, when the muscles lay on the glass surface and the spinal cord on the conducting plate; but on the contrary they became more violent when the spinal cord was placed on the glass plate and the muscles on the conducting plate; but sometimes of their own accord they became far more vehement and longer, appearing without any use of the arc, and as if recurring, if both muscles and nerves had lain on the same armatured glass surface, especially if either light percussion or motion had been made on the armatured glass surface, so that those trunks of animals were seen to have fallen into the severest spasticity.

But if anyone compares these phenomena with those which we said occurred at first, when namely the muscles and the spinal cord were located on one and the same conducting plate, and contractions were excited either by pressure of a hook against the same plate or by other indicated means, he will easily understand that these were then far less than when similar ones were produced on an armatured glass surface: truly no trifling argument that animal electricity is dissipated less by conducting bodies than is common, ordinary electricity; nevertheless that it is dissipated, and that it is restrained and accumulated by insulating bodies no less than the former, which, if I judge correctly, will appear far more clearly in the subsequent experiments.

For before removing my hand and solicitude from these experiments, I wished to investigate whether the same phenomena of contractions would occur not only on glass or resinous but also on marble or highly polished surfaces, that I might forsooth remove that doubt which was often observed in my mind, whether the contractions, which I myself used to repeat with animal electricity, proceeded rather from the electricity of an armatured glass or resinous surface. Therefore the same experiments were undertaken with armatured marble surfaces as with glass and resinous, and all turned out the same way, but more languid contractions occurred, so that those devices had to be employed whereby the effects of animal electricity exciting contractions are augmented. Hence it was often necessary to equip one surface of one marble plate, or part of it, (for it is the same, whether you employ two plates, or one divided into parts by means of armatures), with one metal, tin for example or silver, and the other with bronze or gold-leaf, in order that contractions might occur; perhaps because animal electricity, like common and ordinary, is wont to be checked less readily by marble than by vitreous or resinous substances.

But this ought not to be passed over in silence, because if the arc should have one extremity of insulating material, and then that should be applied, as above, to the armatured plates, it excites no contractions at all; but they are excited, if either the same extremity, or other insulating body, be applied to armatured nerves, or to the spinal cord, as we have already suggested.

But having observed the phenomenon in dead frogs and in dissected nerves, we were impelled to try the same in living frogs also, both with intact and with dissected nerves. Therefore, the integument having been reflected and the crural nerve exposed and armatured, where it advances completely bare, namely below the place of the leg which can be compared to the ham, we applied the arc as usual both to the same nerve and to the muscles of the leg; contractions occurred not infrequently; but they always occurred when the nerve was dissected and armatured and laid on an armatured glass surface, and then the arc applied either to the nerve, or only to the same surface, and to the muscles, in the same way as before; but contractions were lacking, wholly or in great part, if the plate on which the nerve lay was conductile and had been insulated in no way: so that it seemed thence to be established that the mode of action of animal electricity is exactly the same both in living and in dead animals.

Having had so many, and I think not obscure, indications of the effects of animal electricity, I wished to find out whether, as we noted to occur in ordinary and extrinsic electricity, the customary preparation of nerves and their diligent separation from other parts contributed anything to collecting and manifesting its powers.

Moreover I found that it contributes a great deal. For if with only the cranium or the vertebral column opened, and the rest of the animal intact, the cerebrum or the spinal cord was covered with its own tinfoil, and then one extremity of an arc was applied to an armatured portion and the other to a leg, some contractions occurred in the upper limbs, but none or scarcely any in the lower; but imperceptibly and gradually others appeared, according as the animal was denuded and exenterated, and nerves were more and more separated from adjacent parts, until finally, when all the nerves were isolated and free and surrounded only with bronze-foil, they appeared great and violent, with the same arc and the same method employed, so that it seemed established thence that perchance paths and some access lie open for animal electricity from the nerves to the contiguous parts either through moisture or through lymphatic or blood-vessels accompanying the nerves; and when these are dissected, the nerves are free, and while they remain insulated, electricity prepared for motion, flowing to the armatured place, either wholly or in great part, and completing its circuit through muscles and nerves by means of the arc, produces the contractions far greater than before their preparation.

But that a new phenomenon of this sort exists seems no slight argument for animal electricity: and perhaps some suspicion may arise thence that the acceleration of blood and circulation of humors in the muscular motion depend either principally or in some part on electricity itself, flowing from the nerves to the vessels and making inroad into their humors: and surely, if there were room for this conjecture, perhaps some explanation might emerge thence why in old men, in whom many vessels coalesce, i.e. become occluded from arteriosclerosis, the electricity, hastening more abundantly along the nerves directly to the cerebrum, not infrequently injures the latter seriously, and for this reason also renders old age more susceptible to both paralysis, and apoplexy, and other diseases of this sort. But of these we will speak elsewhere.

But nothing seemed to us to conduce more to deriving some utility from our experiments than diligently to transfer to warm-blooded animals also those which had hitherto been tried in the cold-blooded.

For I readily realized, if those things which I had discovered had pertained only to cold-blooded animals, that I had discovered only

certain of their properties, perhaps hardly associated with any utility: but if the same things could be found also in the warm-blooded,
I was shown great hope that the result would be that I might accomplish not a little towards a little more revealing, if not clearly
explaining, the essence and nature of muscular and nervous powers;
which perhaps without some increase could not be of utility both
to physiology and to medicine.

Moreover, the experiments having been performed, in birds and
in quadrupeds, not once but again and again, not only the principal
phenomena appeared, according to desire, as in cold-blooded animals, namely frogs and turtles, but they both appeared more easily
and were far more conspicuous. It was possible also to observe this
peculiarity in both the living and the dead animal, Figs. 20 and 21,
for example that in a lamb or a chick, with a crural nerve dissected
and covered with metal foil and extended on an armatured glass
surface, contractions were obtained without the device of an arc,
but solely by the contact of some conducting body with the same
surface; but they are never obtained when the nerve is extended on
a metallic surface, unless an arc is applied to the animal according
to custom.

What more fitting, what more certain, than that it should be
demonstrated that animal electricity is diffused to contiguous bodies
by the nerves, and, not otherwise than common and ordinary electricity, is accustomed to be arrested by insulating and dispersed by
conducting substances? These are the things which we have ascertained by experiment.

But finally we wish the reader warned that animal electricity,
discovered by us, just as in many other properties, so chiefly in its
inconstancy, variety, and as it were renewal after a certain time,
corresponds not a little with common electricity. For the contractions differ greatly, particularly those occurring in this last part of
the experiments, not only in accordance with the different kind of
animals, but in accordance with the varied nature, age, condition,
and strength of each of them; so that in some they occur very strong
and promptly, feebly in others, and hardly perceptible: they differ
likewise in accordance with varied seasons of the year, and even with
the condition of the sky itself.

For in summer time and with a sky threatening thunder and lightning, the contractions are accustomed to be stronger and prompter,

than in winter and with a calm sky, although then we have observed that the force with which they are excited in the animal is extinguished more quickly; they are stronger likewise and prompter in the older than in the younger; in the more active than in the more sluggish animal; finally in the exsanguinated and pale than in those filled with blood, and with red muscles.

Moreover, in one and the same prepared animal, there are contractions now scanty, now strong, sometimes even none; and sometimes they occur at initial experiments; sometimes after many trials. Moreover this so great variety of effects or contractions occurs not only at great but also at brief intervals of time.

Finally, diminished after a certain time and certain respite, contractions augment, sometimes as if voluntarily, and grow stronger, nay failing they are also restored as if voluntarily, when other external causes and associated phenomena are barely or not even barely changed, as it appears, not otherwise than as the electricity seems to be refreshed and restored through rest and quiet at a certain time in the magic quadrant or Leyden jar, dissipated by repeated experiments.

But that those who have devoted themselves to this kind of experiments may the better recognize the use and utility of the arc, it aids to note this, that with failing contractions which, especially with armatured nerves, are sometimes excited at the outset by the sole contact of any conducting body, if then they have recourse to the use of the arc, they will see the contractions restored anew; but if they wish to adapt the same arc to the armatured surfaces of a plane, then let them call it into use either continuously or a little after the preparation of the animal.

Moreover, we give this advice with this purpose, lest anyone, in repeating these experiments of ours, in estimating the force of contractions and of electricity, should either deceive himself or think that we have been deceived; for if these same experiments are tried many times, he will find out many times also the phenomena which we have produced by trial and experience.

Part Four

CONJECTURES AND SOME CONCLUSIONS

From what is known and explored thus far, I think it is sufficiently established that there is electricity in animals, which, with Bartholinus and others, we may be permitted to call by the general name of animal electricity. This, if not in all, yet is contained in most parts of animals; but manifests itself most conspicuously in muscles and nerves. The peculiar and not previously recognized nature of this seems to be that it flows from muscles to nerves, or rather from the latter to the former, and that it traverses there either an arc or a series of men or any other conducting bodies which lead from nerves to muscles by a shorter and quicker way, and flows most speedily through them from the former to the latter.

From this, moreover, two consequences seem chiefly to ensue, namely, that the electricity in these parts is, one positive, as we may believe, the other negative, and that one is wholly distinct in nature from the other; for when equilibrium is established, there is no motion, no excursion of electricity, no phenomenon of muscular contraction.

But forsooth, it is difficult to define in which of the designated parts one electricity resides, in which the other; whether, for example, one in muscle, the other in nerve, or both in one and the same muscle, and from which part it flows. In this obscurity of things, however, if it is permissible to have an opinion, my mind inclines towards placing the location of both kinds of electricity in muscle.

For to obtain muscular contractions grant that it is generally necessary to apply one extremity of the arc outside of muscles, the other to muscles, as we have said; but it does not seem to follow thence, because nerves are rich in intrinsic electricity, that therefore one kind has its seat in them and the other in muscles; just as in a Leyden jar, although it is customary that one extremity of the arc should be applied to the external surface thereof, the other to its conductor, in order that the excursion of electricity may be made from one to the other, nevertheless it cannot be inferred therefrom that the electricity which is produced in the conductor is peculiar, and unlike that which collects within the bottom of the jar; nay

even it is established that that looks altogether towards the internal
and charged surface, and that both electricities, although contrary,
are contained in the same flask.

Wherefore, if the great number of contractions obtained
in the prepared animal be considered, for which surely the small
quantity of electricity contained in the small part of the nerve
remaining in the prepared muscles is adequate; if, moreover, the
many arguments be considered which are sought from the animal
functions, which openly declare that the nerve fluid, already demonstrated by us is electric and flows freely and swiftly through the
nerves; if finally the obvious and simple explanation of the phenomena from each electricity be sought residing in the muscle itself:
it will not seem beside the point, as we shall show hereafter, that
the muscle should be the proper seat of the electricity investigated
by us, but that the nerve performs the function of a conductor.

These things being admitted, it would perhaps be a not inept
hypothesis and conjecture, nor altogether deviating from the truth,
which should compare a muscle fibre to a small Leyden jar, or other
similar electric body, charged with two opposite kinds of electricity;
but should liken the nerve to the conductor, and therefore compare
the whole muscle with an assemblage of Leyden jars. Moreover
that a double and opposite electricity can occupy one and the same
muscle he will readily grant not contrary to the truth who has considered that a muscular fibre, although at first sight very simple,
nevertheless is composed of diverse solid and liquid parts, which
produce in it no slight variety of substance: certainly the sensation
which is present at every point of the fibre warns us clearly that
nerve substance is found in it altogether different from muscle. And
indeed, although, at whatever point of the fibre, this nerve substance neither constitutes the nerve, nor is obvious to the eyes, but
is diagnosed by sensation alone, what prevents us from conjecturing
that it is in some part different from the substance of visible nerve,
or disposed in a different way, and that therefore it has an electrical
nature; but that it is extended as a conducting nerve beyond the
muscle fibre? But perhaps this will appear more clearly from that
which we shall say a little later about nerves.

But much less easily could he deny double electricity in one and
the same muscular fibre who should see that it is neither difficult
nor without some sort of truth that the same fibre should have

external and internal surfaces opposite one another, either having observed a cavity, which some assign to it, or from diversity of substances, of which we have said it is composed, which cannot be without various holes and surfaces of the muscular substance.

Finally, if anyone turns his mind even for a short time to the tourmaline stone, in which recent discoveries seem to suggest that a double and opposite electricity is found, he will perceive a new reason derived from analogy, whereby a hypothesis of this sort is rendered not altogether vain. But, however the circumstance is, we have seemed to observe so much agreement of causes and of phenomena between the eruption of electric fluid from a Leyden jar and our contractions, that from this hypothesis and comparison we have barely and not even barely been able to withdraw our mind and restrain ourselves from deriving both the former and the latter from a similar cause.

For particularly by employing three devices, electricity breaks from the internal surface of a Leyden jar; namely by the contact of its conductor with some highly conductile body, by the apposition of an arc, and by the production of a spark from the conductor of an electric machine, as we have most recently observed.

Moreover, with these three devices we have already seen contractions of muscles obtained: namely by contact of an armatured nerve which we have made a muscle conductor; by the application of an arc by its extremities both to the same nerve, and to the muscle; and finally by the passage of a spark.

But just as among those devices, more apt and stronger than all for promoting the eruption of electricity from a Leyden jar is the arc, so we have already seen that it is more suitable than all for exciting muscular contractions: likewise, just as, unless the conductor projects beyond the orifice of the jar, and especially extends beyond that on which rests and in which is contained the conducting material inside the jar, the use of the arc can do hardly anything to induce these muscular contractions, if the nerves were resected close to the muscles; as we have already demonstrated.

But now with respect to the production of a spark, the similarity proceeds even farther than we have hitherto explained; but in order that it may be rightly understood, we have noticed that, when by chance it was made dark, we have observed a luminous pencil to gleam continuously from the pointed conductor of a charged Leyden jar and then after some time to fail spontaneously. But after it failed, if the jar were placed at a certain distance from the conductor of the machine and a spark elicited from the same conductor, again the same pencil appeared at the very moment of time when the spark was produced, but soon vanished, and so the produced spark alternately arises and is extinguished. It is a pencil of this sort which, tested and investigated by us in various ways presented a new and not inconsiderable argument for the analogy already proposed.

For as a pencil of this sort appears at the passage of a spark, contractions are excited, as we suggested; moreover, just as if a conducting body, especially one communicating with the earth, be applied to the external surface of the jar just at the time when the same pencil either fails or languishes at the passage of the spark, the spark, again elicited, continuously revives and is restored; so, if the same conducting body be applied to muscles, we have already suggested that the contractions of muscles were either restored when failing or augmented when languishing, while sparks were being elicited. Likewise, in order that that pencil may appear, when a spark is produced, whether the conductor faced the machine of the jar or were in the opposite region; so then, as we have said, contractions occur, whether the nerves and their conductors were from the region of the machine, or in the opposite direction. But when the tube is either glass or resinous, if that part of the conductor be occluded, which projects beyond the orifice of the jar, the pencil fails at the passage of the spark, not otherwise than as contractions fail when nerves are enclosed in the same tube, although the rest of the animal is freely exposed to the air.

Moreover, just as, if the jar is placed inside another glass vessel covered externally with metallic foil, a failing pencil is restored and revived, when languishing, by sole contact of the exterior of this vessel, while a spark is being elicited; so if the jar, in which is the animal, be placed within the same vessel, as in Fig. 3, Tab. I, contractions languishing, at the passage of a spark, revive by contact of the same vessel; and if they cease, they arise again.

But as all appearance of that electric pencil vanishes at the passage of a spark, either if the conductor of the internal surface does not project, or even if it does, if another conductor is added to it, and this is extended as far as to the external surface of the jar; so, as we have stated, contractions cease on the passage of a spark, if either the nerve does not project beyond the muscles corresponding to it, and the contiguous parts, or if it does project, if another conductor be applied thereto, which is directed as far as to the muscles or to their conductors.

But indeed, although this hypothesis and comparison present no slight appearance of truth, nevertheless there are some things which seem not slightly to oppose them. For either nerves are of an insulative nature, as some surmise, and cannot then perform the function of conductors; or they are conductive: and how then could it be that the electric fluid should be contained within them and not be permitted to escape and diffuse to neighboring parts, not without great detriment surely of muscular contractions?

But this inconvenience and difficulty will easily be met by him who imagines the nerves so constituted that they are hollow within, or composed of some material suitable for conveying electric fluid, but externally they are either oily or are fused with some other substance which prevents the effusion and dissipation of the said electric fluid running through them. Such a structure indeed, and that composition of the nerves, will bring it about that they can perform both functions, namely of conducting the neuro-electric fluid and at the same time of avoiding the effusion thereof, and will be admirably accommodated both for the animal economy and for experiments; if indeed the animal economy seems always to demand animal spirits forced within the nerves; but experiments demonstrate that the nerves consist chiefly of oily substance.

For not only a large amount of oil is obtained by distillation from nerves, and far greater than from muscles, but as a greater quantity of inflammable gas was produced from them by us by a newer method than it was ever possible to elicit from any other part of the animal, and this gas was of such a nature that, when ignited, it emitted a more vivid, purer, and long-lasting flame than the inflammable gas derived from other parts is wont; surely this is no slight indication of more abundant oily substance in nerves.

Nor indeed will this non-conducting substance in nerves, which seems to be a safeguard lest the electric nerve fluid should be dispersed, not without severe detriment, be an impediment lest the same fluid, running out through the intimate conducting substance of nerves, when there is need, should go out from the same nerves, for the accomplishment of contractions, and should be transferred very swiftly through the arc to the muscles according to its custom and nature.

For just as, although the conductor of a Leyden jar is covered with wax, nevertheless, if an arc is applied to it, an explosion is obtained, if either the layer of wax were thin, or, though thicker, were yet covered with a thin metallic foil, provided it does not pass certain limits of thickness, as we have often found; so, from a nerve made in the same way by nature and armatured by art, electric fluid can escape and produce contractions.

Let us therefore be permitted to follow a not improbable hypothesis of this sort, which however we will immediately discard, as soon as either learned men dissent from it, or the discoveries of physicists or new experiments undertaken in respect to it have demonstrated another more suitable.

Now a few things about the nature of animal electricity chosen from those which it is permissible to infer from the described experiments. This electricity, then, has some things in common with artificial and with ordinary electricity, some things with that of the torpedo and other animals of this class.

Things in common with ordinary electricity are: First, free and easy passage through the same bodies through which common electricity is accustomed to pass, namely through metals, among the foremost, and, among these, through the more perfect and nobler, such as gold and silver, then through the less noble, namely copper, iron, tin and lead, moreover through the imperfect metals, such as antimony, and finally through minerals; likewise free and easy passage through water and moist bodies; more difficult passage through stones, earth, and wood; finally, interrupted and completely cut off through glass, resin, and oily substances: wherefrom it results that if metals are laid on an insulating plane, it is inevitable that common and artificial electricity should accumulate in them, and they would be wont to produce far greater effects, namely to excite more violent and longer contractions, than if the same metals communicated freely with other conducting bodies.

Second, the choice, in excursion, of a shorter and quicker way, an arc, for example, or angles, or points.

Third, a double and opposite nature, namely one positive, the other negative.

Fourth, daily and hourly constant attachment to muscles not otherwise than common electricity is wont by nature to electric bodies.

Fifth, spontaneous restoration, not lasting a short space of time.

Sixth, distinct increase of power by employment of the device of a so-called armature made of the same metal with which the physicists are accustomed to surround resinous and vitreous bodies.

Properties in common with electricity of the torpedo and other animals of this class are chiefly these:—

Namely, as it were, a sort of circulation of electricity from one part of the animal to another, and this either through an arc or through the fluid itself of the arc alternately, as the physicists have observed. Whereby forsooth it is established that such a circulation is characteristic, not of the torpedo alone or of similar animals but perhaps of animals generally when our devices are employed. Moreever, as in the latter so in the former, there are absent both sensation of a relatively gentle breeze, and attraction or repulsion of very light bodies, and finally indications of the slightest motion in electrometers hitherto invented.

But even our animal electricity has this in common with this kind of electricity, that it requires no previous device, friction for example, heat or other things of this sort, by which it should be excited, but it is ready as if by nature and continually prompt, and is produced on contact alone.

Nay, so great promptness for action is in this electricity of animals, which we have experienced, that if the vertebral column is allowed to be touched by an insulating body in a place where it is armatured, not rarely contractions are produced, particularly if the animal has been recently slaughtered and prepared. Moreover, they often occur if the same insulating body is so pressed against metallic foil that the contact of the foil with the nerve emerging from the vertebral column is either augmented or changed, but I know not whether this can be affirmed concerning the torpedo's electricity.

Moreover, this one thing seems particularly proper and peculiar of the torpedo and cognate animals that at their will and pleasure they can direct electricity outside the skin, and expel it so that it completes its circulation outside the body, and with such quantity and force that it exhibits a spark, if we heed the physicists, so that it produces a concussion and violent sensation and sometimes makes such an impact on the animalcules that fall into the path of its circulation, that it either kills or stupefies and terrifies them. But perhaps in animals of this class this indicates more abundant quantity and force, not really a different nature; and perhaps some time, devices can be found whereby effects of this sort can be obtained in other animals also.

Moreover, electric circulations of this sort, discovered and described by us in other animals, not only their strength and relations but also their ways and instruments, perhaps will be able to shed some light on the same circulation in the torpedo and cognate animals, and again from more diligent discussion and observation of these animal organs which are fitted for this function, these of ours will be able to receive light. The instruments perhaps will be similar, and the terminals of the electric circuit, namely muscles and nerves, the same.

These things concerning the nature and character of animal electricity: now a few things concerning its source. This I should think to be not dissimilar from that which physiologists, up to the present time, have indicated for animal spirits, namely the cerebrum. For though we have indicated that electricity is inherent in muscles, yet we do not concur in the opinion that it emanates from them also, as from its proper and natural source.

For since all nerves, both those to the muscles and those which go to other parts of the body, seem to be altogether the same, as in kind so in nature, who will rightfully deny that all carry fluid of the same nature? But already we have shown above that electric fluid is carried through the nerves of muscles; therefore it will be carried through all: therefore from one common source, namely the cerebrum, they will drain it, from the source and origin of all: for otherwise there would be as many sources as there are parts in which nerves terminate; and although these are very different in nature and construction, they do not seem suited for the elaboration and secretion of one and the same fluid.

Therefore we believe it equally true that electricity is prepared by action of the cerebrum, and that it is extracted from the blood, and that it enters the nerves, and that it runs through them within, whether they are hollow and free, or whether, as seems more probable, they carry a very thin lymph, or some other peculiar similar thin fluid, secreted, as many think, by the cortical cerebrum. If this prove so, the obscure nature of animal spirits, long sought in vain, may perhaps appear clearly. But as things are, certain no one of those hereafter, I think, after these experiments of ours, will call electricity into doubt. And although, led merely by reason and by some observations, we first brought this into our public Anatomical Amphitheater, and many illustrious men had already mentioned it before, yet never might we think fortune sufficiently favorable to us to grant to us perchance first to handle it, as it were with our hands, lurking in the nerves, and to draw it out of the nerves, and almost to place it under our eyes.

With these premises and indications, I now turn for the first time to those things which pertain to some explanation especially of the muscular contractions which are obtained by our experiments, thence to bring forward those which pertain not only to natural and voluntary motions, but also to involuntary and pathological, in order that some approach may be opened to utility of our observations, if indeed it may be permissible to transfer these data of ours, as not without cause we think, from animals, and especially from the warm-blooded, to man.

Now from the experiments performed, this fact emerges without difficulty, that there is a swift and violent excursion of neuro-electric fluid through the muscle to that nerve whereby chiefly muscular contractions and motions are excited.

But in what way an excursion of this kind of electricity causes and induces contractions, whether, for example, by some mechanical irritation and stimulus striking either the nerves or the muscle fibre and, as they say, exciting the irritability thereof, or, by the custom and character of common electric vapor, exciting a peculiar and violent attraction between the particles composing, for example, a muscle fibre, by its swift excursion through it, so that, as they mutually approach one another, the fibre becomes shorter; or whether, as is easier to believe, it is acting for some other reason not yet understood, is a very difficult thing to be known, and very much involved in darkness. More and more experiments undertaken on this subject may perhaps bring some light some time. But now that first comes into question, in what way and from what causes does such an excursion of electricity from the muscles to the nerves occur in the experiments described, which will not be difficult to find under the hypothesis previously described.

In the first place, therefore, I should wish it carefully noted that two things are either chiefly requisite, or certainly highly conducive to exciting muscular contractions, about which we have heretofore discussed.

First, namely, something which shall attract the neuro-electric fluid from the muscle to the nerve and instigate it to exit; then something which shall receive it as it goes out from the nerve and either take it back and as it were restore it to the muscles or conduct it elsewhere and dissipate it. Indeed, if one or the other of that conditions is lacking, the phenomenon of contractions will be lacking also.

Now the things which invite and as it were force neuro-electric fluid from the muscle to the nerve seem to be chiefly these: namely, the suddenly removed equilibrium between the internal electricity of muscles and nerves and the external electricity of bodies communicating chiefly with nerves; moreover, irritation of the same nerves; contact of some body, principally conducting, either with the same nerves themselves or with conducting bodies communicating with the same nerves; finally, as it were, some disturbance of the substance, or friction of the slightest sort, as when, by simple percussion of the plane on which the prepared animal is lying, contractions are excited.

Moreover, it is clear that stimuli of this sort can finally be referred partly to disturbed equilibrium, partly to some kind of impulse into nerves, even if very slight.

But the electric fluid, running to a nerve for these reasons, will be received by some conducting body, which will transfer it from the nerves to the muscles, if it was produced from the former to the latter by use of the electric arc; but it will convey it elsewhere, if it has communicated with nerves alone, or with bodies touching nerves, and if it has a certain magnitude.

But, these things having been noted and determined, I come to the explanation of the muscular motions which we have observed, and first of those which are obtained at the extortion of a spark.

For at the passage of a spark, electricity breaks out both from the layers of air surrounding the conductor of the machine and from the nerve-conductors communicating with the same layers; and negative electricity results on account of them. Hence the intrinsic positive electricity of muscles runs to the nerves both with its own strength and with strength from extrinsic electricity, more abundant whether you borrow it from artificial or natural, as received from their conductors, and flowing through them, failing both in them and in the shortly hitherto mentioned layers of air, it will renew the electricity, and establish itself at equilibrium therewith; not otherwise than as, in a Leyden jar, the positive electricity of the internal surface in the production of a spark, flows more abundantly to the conductor of the former, for the same reasons, and goes out therefrom, just as the form of a luminous electric pencil openly declares.

Hence it is understood without difficulty whether there is utility or necessity in the nerves of conductors for receiving and transferring electricity and their constant ratio and proportion with muscular contractions.

Similar seem to be the cause and reason of the muscular contractions which are obtained, on the passage of a spark, in an animal enclosed in our little glass machine: for the intrinsic electricity of the muscles seems to flow to the internal surface of the glass through the nerves and their conductors on account of the same law of equilibrium, so that forsooth as much electricity collects at the internal surface of the glass as had been removed from the external surface by passage of the spark.

The reason and cause of the phenomenon seems the same also in the contractions which occur when the conductors of prepared animals are applied to the external surface of a Leyden jar, or near it, when a spark is elicited from the conductor of the internal surface.

Indeed, so aptly and clearly is the phenomenon explained by this law of surfaces and of equilibrium, that I should not easily blame him who explained also by the same law those contractions which are obtained in the extortion of a spark from the conductor of an electric machine, and who should consider the same conductor as a double surface in the surrounding layers of air, one an internal conductor, the other external as regards the animal.

But whether it happens for this or that reason, or any other, not yet known, no one will doubt that the causes and reasons of the phenomenon are the same in those contractions which we said occur in thunderstormy weather; for at the cast of thunderbolts the same thing is seen to befall the layers of air surrounding the electric cloud as befalls those which surround the electric machine.

Finally, there is no one who does not see that, from the same law of equilibrium between the positive electricity of muscles and the negative electricity of sealing-wax, those contractions easily take their origin which we said occur when the same rubbed wax is applied to nerves, but fail when rubbed glass is applied; likewise that from the same law of equilibrium those contractions also derive which we have already warned will occur when the shield of an electrophore is raised from its resinous surface.

But I come now to those contractions which are excited either by an arc, or by the contact of conducting bodies with nerves, or by irritation of the same nerves, or in other ways which we have indicated above; and indeed no one has even briefly considered what of animal electricity pertains to them, how we have referred its nature and character, without easily understanding how those are devices suitable and adapted for attracting the positive internal electricity of the muscles to the nerves, and receiving it and, as we have stated, for negatively transferring it to the external electric part of muscles.

But, these things being once admitted, it may be enquired how it is that, if a nerve is even touched briefly by some insulating body, as happens sometimes if it were armatured, it is irritated by the same or, if you prefer, by artificial electricity, nevertheless contractions appear.

For then indeed there is present both contact and impulse which, though perhaps slight, could recall neuro-electric fluid to the exterior of a nerve: but the body which should receive the same fluid and either conduct it elsewhere for the sake of equilibrium, or restore it much more to the muscles, seems to be wholly lacking.

But if the phenomena described are accurately weighed, and the nature and character of neuro-electric fluid considered, which is accustomed to find free access and a ready way for itself only through conducting bodies, and to hasten swiftly from nerves to muscles, perhaps not even then will the conducting body of an arc seem necessary as an alternate; forsooth, the fluid and moist external parts of nerves, or particularly their thick and hard membranes, or both, will be able to perform this function. Hence perhaps with the cranium open and the cerebrum exposed, and likewise the spinal cord removed from its vertebral column and bare, no contractions of muscles, as we have said, are excited, even if an arc be applied; but they are excited, if the same be equipped with metallic foil, which goes far towards taking the place of the missing membrane;

but it happens otherwise, as we have warned in nerves which, although nature has covered them with thick membranes outside the cerebrum, it is always useful, though not necessary, to provide with metallic foil. But if you compare the metallic foil, with which we are accustomed to cover nerves, as it were to part of the arc, and recall to mind what we reported concerning the utility of multiple arc substance in augmenting contractions, perhaps those of the contractions which, as we have already said, seemed to occur only on contact, you will generally repeat from the arc also which is as it were composed partly of metallic foil, partly of the already mentioned conducting substances of nerves.

But if these things be granted, perhaps some approach will be opened to explaining the muscular motions which occur in the living animal, and which we now advance to consider. For what pertains to voluntary motions, perhaps the mind, with its marvelous power, might make some impetus either into the cerebrum, as is very easy to believe, or outside the same, into whatever nerve it pleases, wherefrom it will result that neuro-electric fluid will quickly flow from the corresponding muscle to that part of the nerve to which it was recalled by the impetus, and when it has arrived there, the insulating part of the nerve substance being overcome through its then increased strength, as it goes out thence, it will be received either by the extrinsic moisture of the nerve, or by the membranes, or by other contiguous conducting parts, and through them, as through an arc, will be restored to the muscle from which, as we are pleased to think, it previously flowed out, from the positively electric part of the same, through impulse in the nerve.

Perhaps in no dissimilar, though less difficult way, if I am any judge, the occurrence could be hastened in involuntary and unusual movements, namely if sharp and stimulating agents irritate the nerves, or the spinal cord, or the cerebrum, and at the same time summon the neural fluid, so that, having been received by the conducting parts, it is finally restored to the muscles as if through an arc.

But in accordance with the different power and faculty of the acid humors for stimulation and conduction, the contractions also will be dissimilar; likewise in accordance with the different location which they will occupy in the nervous parts.

For it is easy to understand, when humors of this sort are poured out of the vessels and subside between the surface of the nerve-substance and its investments, that contractions then ought to become more violent and longer; because then, forsooth, the effused and the stagnant acid humors will not only irritate the nerve more severely, but will also constitute, as it were, a more suitable kind of armature and arc for the neuro-electric fluid.

Hence, in the more severe rheumatic affections, and particularly in nervous sciatica, in which, according to Cotunius, the humor stagnates between the sheath and the surface of the nerve, not only are the pains more severe, but there are wont to be severe and constant contractions of the muscles of the affected joint, so that often the said joint may remain either long or permanently contracted.

Hence perhaps even such violent, such long, so readily and at brief intervals recurrent, and generally fatal contractions of the muscles, or convulsions occur when acid and perverted humors stagnate either within the cerebrum and the pia mater, or within the pia mater and the dura mater, or within the cerebral ventricles, or within the surface of the spinal cord or of the nerves and their investments, as generally happens in tetanus, in which disease it becomes chiefly noteworthy that at first nearly all the muscles fall into very severe tonic contractions, although sometimes only one nerve may be affected for a short time, as in the tetanus which sometimes follows the puncture of a nerve; then it is noteworthy that the muscles relapse into the same contractions, both spontaneously and often only and when by a slight tremor or percussion of the bed, or surface on which the bed of the patient is resting. But we have already seen something similar happen, in prepared and armatured animals in whom it is permitted that an arc should be applied briefly to one crural nerve, nevertheless all the muscles not only of one limb, but of both, fell into tonic contractions, and sometimes recurred into them spontaneously, either from a mere tremor, or from percussion, of the surface on which the animals were lying, so that on this account these experiments of ours on this disease and its peculiar symptoms seem, if not to have discovered the cause and reason, at least to have injected some suspicion into the doctors.

Now, indeed, these theories concerning contractions of muscles, both gentle and natural, more violent, and pathological, having been postulated and considered, it was inevitable that there should be presented to my mind as it were a new cause and reason for the opposite faults, namely paralysis and others, namely the already explained arrested circulation of neuro-electric fluid, either from muscle to nerve, or from nerve to muscle.

First, perhaps, it might happen, if a substance of oily or other insulating nature should beset part of the nerve; second, if a similar material should involve either the external moisture of the nerve, or the membranes themselves, or some other parts, through which the neuro-electric fluid performs its already indicated circulation; but if the effusion and congestion of this material is promoted by acid and especially by corroding agents, the substance and texture both of the nerves and of the cerebrum may be injured. But although perhaps it seems possible that these things may have some truth, particularly in those paralyses and apoplexies which invade patients slowly and step by step, yet, in those which attack them in a moment of time, it seemed that a far different cause of the phenomenon must be considered.

While I was revolving these and similar ideas in my mind, there was presented to me as it were a new cause not only of apoplexy but of epilepsy, derived chiefly from those things which are often observed to occur when artificial electricity is employed in animals.

For just as when artificial electricity is industriously directed either against the cerebrum, or against the nerves, or against the spinal cord, for example by means of the conductor of a Leyden jar, if it rushes into those parts with a certain quantity and force, it irritates them and throws the animals into violent convulsions; but if it injures and violently impairs their substance with a far greater quantity, it renders the same animals paralytic or apoplectic, or, if it were more violent, destroys them: so I conjectured that animal electricity could do the same or similar things in man, especially if, as common electricity is wont, especially if it should seize and promptly add to itself those delicate elements whereby far greater power might be added to it; of which sort would be what come under the name of acid elements, whatever those might be; and so I thought that now epilepsy, now apoplexy could be induced by thus contaminated animal electricity hastening through the nerves either from the muscles or from other parts to the cerebrum and rushing into it, according as its force and impetus into the substance of the cerebrum were more or less, and its contamination more or less severe. For it seemed that the excursion and impetus of animal electricity could be violently summoned through the nerves to the cerebrum by the quantity and quality of the depraved humors stagnating in the said brain, and stimulating and injuring the brain itself or the nerves, or finally, to pass over other things, by any great and sudden mutation of atmospheric electricity, especially if its conversion from positive to negative is made abruptly, perhaps not unlike that which we conjecture both the conductor of the electric machine and the electric cloud to produce in the surrounding atmospheric layers, either at the extortion of a spark, or at the crash of a thunderbolt.

Now thus far I assumed that no one failed to see how the causes reviewed could exercise their forces more violently, promptly and easily, if acid and stimulating materials were clinging in the cerebrum, than if in the nerves; for in the former they may well designate those diseases as idiopathic, but in the latter as symptomatic: and moreover diseases of this sort will be also far more severe, and will occur more readily, if animal electricity, and contaminated at that, is in excess in the body and particularly in the muscular and nervous parts. Hence I reflected that diseases of this sort are particularly prevalent in old men, because in them a more abundant supply of contaminated animal electricity seems to accumulate, both on account of their intermitted labors and exercises, and because of the dryness of the parts induced by old age, and primarily the density of the oily substance of nerves, and finally because of the diminished insensible perspiration by which so great an amount both of electricity and, of acid and delicate principles is carried outside the body; so also I conjectured that these fatal diseases prevail for the same reason especially when those more severe storms and changes of weather are threatening, in which there is wont to be a greater quantity of electricity in the atmosphere, or a little afterwards; for at that time more electricity is found in animals, so that the contractions described, then occurring more often and more promptly and more violently, seem clearly significant. For these and for other reasons, then, immoderately increased and contaminated animal electricity seemed with such force and impetus to be able to rush and flow into the substance of the cerebrum in a moment of time that in the same moment of time it injured its structure severely, and ruptured vessels, whence both paralysis constantly and easily followed and humors were poured out, and having been shed and stagnating, as often happens, were found in sections of corpses.

These and other things used to come into my mind about the cause and the manner of invasion of these diseases; but at the same time I realized that hypotheses of this sort could incur many and grave difficulties among learned men and perhaps their reprehension for many reasons, and particularly because they oppose the opinion, common and accepted in the schools, namely that muscular motions are performed by an excursus of nerve fluid from the cerebrum to the muscular parts, not from the latter to the former. But if anyone among other things should recall to mind that aura, as it were, which, ascending to the cerebrum either from the lower limbs, or from the stomach, or from the lower abdomen, epileptics easily and very often feel and accuse at the moment when they are seized with convulsions; if then he should consider that sometimes the progress of this disease is arrested, if a noose or tourniquet is applied to the leg, which, as it were, impedes and intercepts the way: if anyone, I say, turns his attention to all these things and to our experiments, he will easily pardon us, if we have descended to these conjectures. But these things, as I was saying, I was, as it were, imagining in my mind, chiefly with this purpose, that they might be recalled to consideration by the most learned scholars.

A cause having been suggested, not only of natural but also of pathological contractions, and the cause of paralysis having been sought chiefly in the ascertained nature of animal electricity, there seem to remain some things which should be touched on concerning the treatment of these diseases.

And in the first place it seems that this can be derived from our experiments, that, whatever remedies are employed for removing those diseases, and even electricity itself administered externally, all these things, if they are going to do any good ought to exercise their effect chiefly on animal electricity, and either increase or diminish it or change it in some other way. Which electricity, therefore, and its status the doctor should have chiefly before his eyes in treatment.

Therefore, omitting other remedies, whose effect on electricity of animals diligent investigation and use will reveal and disclose some day, I immediately turn to the administration of external electricity, and, in order that the thing may proceed more clearly, I will consider it first in convulsive and rheumatic contractions of muscles, then in paralysis.

But before all, a threefold faculty and function in applying artificial electricity to the human body, in my judgment at least, comes under consideration; first, namely, that which can be called, as it were, extemporaneous, and which continuously exerts action on parts of the human body which are exposed to it, as when it acts through a spark, and especially through an electric thunderbolt, as it were, when a Leyden jar is discharged; second, when electricity produces its action not continuously but successively and with the passage of time, combined perhaps, and almost I had said with chemicals, combined especially with the fluid parts of the animal body, as that electricity which the younger physicists call balneal; finally at length that which draws electricity from the animal, as when negative electricity, as the same physicists call it, is employed.

Let us now consider briefly these individual functions in the diseases mentioned. Now as for what pertains to convulsive contractions of muscles, anyone easily sees that, in our hypothesis, these generally derive either from exuberant and contaminated animal electricity in the muscles, which, for most trivial causes is summoned from the muscles to the nerves and to the cerebrum, or particularly from acid and stimulating principles striking either the brain or the nerves, or, as often happens, from both causes. If the first, it seems that positive electricity, as they say, could scarcely, and not even scarcely, afford any benefit, but rather more injury, in whatever way administered; but negative electricity, as is obvious, might be of no slight advantage. But if it were the second, the physician can promise himself some benefit from positive electricity, if this is artificially directed to the affected nerves; for this can, by its own power, repel and remove acid principles from the nerves.

On account of these things, the differential diagnosis of convulsions and their causes should be diligently attended to and investigated by the physician: and although perchance both causes may often be present, nevertheless it should be sedulously considered which of them is more powerful, and although this is difficult, yet not all hope is to be abandoned that sometime we may be able at length nevertheless to accomplish this. Since, for example, there may be some not slight indications of exuberant electricity, a present or slightly previous amount of electricity in the atmosphere, and our experiments prove how much this augments the powers and effects of electricity.

Moreover a quantity of this sort can be explored and diagnosticated by the device of atmospheric electrometers, and also by the appearance of the clouds, by the time and season of year, by the tempests of heaven, by the qualities of winds, by the phases of the moon, and by other signs handed down by illustrious physicists, and foremost by Bartholinus and Gardiner. Besides these, an excess of electricity in us can also be indicated by a certain unwonted speed and alacrity of motions, especially of the eyes, deriving from no other obvious cause, combined with the greatest variety and inconstancy.

Likewise perhaps suspicion might be moved by those very mutations which artificial electricity is accustomed to produce in us, namely unwonted internal warmth, increased secretions and excretions, as of bowels, urine, saliva, sweat, insensible perspiration, rapidity, magnitude and vibration of the pulses, moreover the use of foods in which the idioelectric or insulating principles are contained, as of aromatous, oily, and spirituous liquors, especially if perhaps no other causes of these mutations are apparent. Certainly these are generally accustomed to precede especially the more severe convulsions, and other affections of the nerves, such as epilepsy, mania, and others similar.

Moreover, the opposite could warn us clearly of negative or deficient electricity. But, indeed, if there were any indications of perverted or contaminated electricity, they will perhaps be furnished by some of the discomforts of patients and symptoms of diseases, which to the doctors are wont to signify the power and prevalence of acid principles. But let it suffice to have touched upon these, that another way may be open to investigate and diagnose the varied status of animal electricity.

But as for what pertains to rheumatic contractures of the muscles, since these generally take their principal origin from acid and stimulating material settling in nerves, it is easy to surmise that in them almost individual methods of administering positive electricity could be useful, employed, however, in the following order and plan; that first that method should be employed which is called "through the bath", for collecting more abundant electricity in the muscles; then that which is administered through sparks; finally that which is

administered through concussion; so that first, forsooth the stagnating humors may be attenuated by the mechanical and repellent
force of electricity, and then more easily removed from the affected
part by increased impulse.

And no less, for the same reason, could negative electricity also
be advantageously applied in the affected part, particularly by our
method, namely by the extortion of a spark either from the conductor of an electric machine or from a Leyden jar, particularly if
the affected part is applied to its conductors, of which some incline
to the machine, others communicate with the ground, which method
could perhaps be rendered more useful, if either large Leyden jars
were employed, or many of them attached to one common conductor,
or larger electric machines, such as in our times are constructed
without difficulty; or much more, if a way should be found whereby
it is possible to direct and impel animal electricity from certain
muscles to certain nerves. For it escapes no one that, of those which
we have suggested, by this method a more vigorous excursion of
animal electricity is promoted particularly through the affected
nerves, most suitable, as it seems, above others, as an aid for dislodging, dissolving, and expelling from the nerves principles stagnant and impacted in them. Hence perhaps muscular motions, which,
as we have said, perhaps arise from the excursion of electricity from
a muscle to the nerves, are accustomed to afford no little benefit
and relief in rheumatic affections, and the more, the more vigorously
the affected parts are moved, even if with some inconvenience and
pain.

But if this new method of administering negative electricity should
be combined with some utility, either in these diseases or in others,
how much greater benefits shall we be able to promise from atmospheric electricity, if, as we have suggested in artificial electricity,
the affected parts by their own conductors are cautiously and pru-
dently adjusted, for example, to the raging thunderbolts and lightnings: was this perhaps the reason why limbs, either contractured
from an early age or paralyzed by disease, have recovered their
natural flexibility, strength, and power of spontaneous motion after
thunderbolts have fallen not far from the patients?

But as to what concerns the treatment of paralysis, I see the subject full of difficulty and danger; for it is difficult to diagnosticate
whether a disease arises from damaged and impaired structure of

nerves or of brain, or from insulating material blocking either the internal parts of a nerve or others whereby we think that the circulation of electricity in us is performed. If it can do little good, and perhaps artificial electricity could do much harm, in whatever way administered; if the latter, it seems that it could afford some utility, either for dislodging insulating material, or for augmenting the strength of animal electricity. But some time perhaps use and experience will reveal the whole subject. But now in closing let us touch on some neither trivial nor useless conclusions from our experiments.

From these, then, it seems to be established that both artificial and atmospheric electricity have far greater power over muscles and nerves than was hitherto recognized; and that from their strength especially as great a faculty passes into animal electricity as in our experiments it was seen that animal electricity has for motion and to promote its exit from the muscles and its speeding passage along nerves, and to excite violent contractions of the muscles.

Moreover, with these things recognized, there is perhaps greater access than it before seemed could lie open for newly discovered and more useful methods of administering electricity than those hitherto ascertained, or for disclosing the causes of agreement between the vicissitudes of atmospheric electricity and of our own health, and between some diseases and the sudden changes of the former.

Moreover such experiments seem to suggest that, in the passages of thunderbolts and of sparks, not only atmospheric, but perhaps also terrestrial, electricity flows back towards heaven. Or indeed does it result from this reflux that, when great storms arise in heaven, mutations and vicissitudes occur in the atmospheric air, not only on account of principles of diverse kind which it transfers from various regions of heaven, but also on account of those which it transfers with itself from earth into the air, if the electric fluid possesses this property, which very many physicists concede to it, that, of the bodies through which it passes, it expels and dissipates some of the more subtle principles, but removes others and joins them to itself? But let the physicists chiefly attend to these matters!

But when such a reflux of terrestrial electricity into the atmosphere occurs, it could claim for itself either a large, or certainly no mediocre part in those swifter and great increases of plants which the illustrious Gardiner observed after lightning and thunder, and ascribed particularly to atmospheric electricity associated with vapors.

Finally, since such contractions of muscles which we have said occur under storms in heaven afford, as it were, a new and not uncertain indication of atmospheric electricity and its effects on the animal economy, these could perhaps conduce no little towards revealing, not so much causes for earthquakes, as effects in the same economy; so that on this account it seems not useless to investigate these same things when earthquakes are raging.

But let there be a limit to conjectures! And now the end.

These were chiefly the things which I communicated to the most learned men as ascertained about the effects of both artificial, and atmospheric, and tempestuous, and natural, electricity on muscular motion which is subject to the will, in order that they might some time bring about that utility which has been most in our desires.

But what things pertain to the effects of these electricities on natural motions, on circulation of the blood and secretion of the humors, these things we will publish as soon as possible in another commentary, when we have found a little more leisure.

Two Letters of
Bassano Carminati and Luigi Galvani

Letter from Don Bassano Carminati
Public Professor of Medicine in the University of Pavia,
to Doctor Luigi Galvani, Bologna

I have delayed until now to thank you for the precious gift which, through the courtesy of our mutual friend, Don Mariano Fontana, you have made me of the dissertation containing your beautiful, original discovery on the natural and spontaneous electricity of animals; I have delayed, I say, until now, in order to offer you, with my own most sincere congratulations, those also of other of my celebrated colleagues, and especially of Spallanzani, of Barletti, of Volta, of Rezia, and of Malacarne, who feel with me all the importance of this your marvellous discovery, and load you with deserved praises. But if, through divided motive, I have not been among the most solicitous to congratulate you, I shall perhaps have at least the merit of imparting to you before anyone else the favorable judgment of your observations and experiments which has been given by one of the best judges whom I know in such matters, that is to say our most distinguished knight and my celebrated colleague, Signor Volta, to whom first I communicated your dissertation, confident that he would not fail to repeat your principal experiments, to vary them, to make new ones, and to carry farther than would otherwise have been possible the researches on a point so fertile of consequences most important in the physical history of the animals. Now he has communicated to me some results of his experiments made in these last eight days since he began to occupy himself with them; and I make haste to report it, flattering myself that in amends I am doing a gracious thing, opportune to bring into greater light a discovery which does so much honor to all Italy.

And first as to artificial electricity applied to frogs prepared in various ways, either cut up or entire, he has observed that their sensitivity, or irritability, is remarkable in all cases, though varying according to the different preparations: being greater in the decapitated than in the entire frog, especially when a needle is driven into the dorsal spine and the electricity made to pass through this route to the extremity of the hind legs: much more after the frog is cut in such a way that only the legs remain and these attached to the spine by the two crural nerves, everything else being removed; and incomparably more still, if this spine and parts of the said nerves are covered with delicate metallic foil. Up to this point, then, his experiments agree with yours, which are found by me, and by others, most accurate, and described with all frankness and with greater elegance.

But the most illustrious Signor Volta has wished to proceed to determine and reduce to degrees and measure the force of the electricity required in all these cases to excite in muscles the contractions and the movements of your descriptions. He has found, then, that, for the live and intact frog, an electricity that is barely sparkling suffices, and that it raises the electrometer quadrant of Henly eight or ten degrees, and even less suffices of the electric charge of the Leyden jar, that is, five or six degrees, placing the frog in the circuit of the discharge. When the frog is decapitated, with the needle fixed in the aforesaid manner, there suffice of the electricity of a simple conductor, if this is reasonably large, three or four degrees of the same electrometer, or less of the charge of a Leyden jar.

When, then, the frog is prepared in the manner already indicated, so that the dorsal spine is connected with the legs only by the crural nerves diligently exposed, a current so weak that it does not move the quadrant electrometer even one degree, and a phial electrometer of Cavallo only eight or ten degrees (with pendula of straw after the manner of the same Signor Volta) is sufficient to produce the customary convulsions in the frog. And employing the Leyden jar, one or two degrees of this same delicate electrometer suffice. But still there is no respect to the sensibility of the animal, when they are wrapped as above, both spine and parts of the nerves, with metallic foil: then less than one tenth of a degree of this same electrometer, which may be the charge of a rather large Leyden jar, produces the effect of convulsing all the muscles of the animal thus prepared.

But how shall one measure so imperceptible a current, which does not even perceptibly move such an electrometer with most delicate little strips of gold foil, after the manner of Bennet? Here our Signor Volta has recourse to his electrical condenser in the English Transactions for the year 1782, and particularly to that of a sort of glove or cap applied to the smooth head of the phial electrometer mentioned: which new device he has described and explained diffusely and elaborately in his letters on electric meteorology, published in the Journal of Dr. Brugnatelli of Pavia, entitled *Physical Library of Europe*.[1]

---

[1] Volume I, 1788.

Such a weak current of electricity, and entirely imperceptible to every other test, producing such manifest effects in the prepared frog, constitutes it an electrometer ten times more sensitive, at least more sensitive with gold foil, for the charges of a strong conductor and of Leyden jars.

Having reduced to this minimum the artificial electricity, which can convulse the frog, Signor Volta concludes that at these limits and moderate degree of force spontaneous electricity acts, or rather intrinsic animal electricity of the animal, when prepared in the same way; its muscles contract and go into convulsions, by simply applying one end of the arc conductor to these muscles, and the other end to the metallic armature of the nerves. Starting from this idea, I thought that he would be able to discover in what part in this little electric machine, or rather Leyden phial, lies the excess, and in what part the deficiency, of electric fluid, despite the inability to show it directly with any electrometer; and he believes that this has been achieved.

I thought to apply the Leyden jar charge at such prodigious weakness as eight or ten hundredths of a degree, entirely imperceptible, as if he said to every electrometer to apply it, or the positive part, to the nerves, and the negative part to the muscles; and now, in a contrary sense, with the idea that where the excess of fluid in the prepared animal was on the side of the nerves and the deficiency on the part of the muscles, the concussion would not ensue from this application to both terminals, nerve and muscle, of homologous electricity, (as no discharge follows testing in the same way two Leyden jars), and on the contrary would follow application of the contrary electricity.

The result corresponded in many tests made in these past two days on three frogs, and especially in one; that is, they had constantly the customary contractions and convulsions, the hook of a Leyden jar applying the charge internally by excess to the nerves, and the body of the same jar to the muscles; and none operating inversely. On the contrary, the phial being negatively charged, convulsions occurred on applying the hook to the muscles and the body to the nerves, and not inversely.

Of course this was true always when the charge of the phial was so weak that it exceeded either none or little the ten hundredths of a degree indicated above: since, when it was four or six times greater, it produced the effect in whatever way it was applied. From these beautiful and delicate experiments, Signor Volta concluded that the deficiency of electric fluid exists on the part of the nerves, not the excess, as you had believed you could advance on other conjectures. Therefore, our distinguished Signor Volta wishes the contrary of your opinion, which is not yet held as a settled thing, because based on experiments of the utmost delicacy, made by him in number, but not yet repeated as much as he would wish.

Meantime, while the above celebrated physicist attends to these experiments on frogs, that they may be perfectly reasonable and easy to perform, let not others among us cease to experiment on other animals, including warm-blooded; and already are verified the tests made by yourself on birds and quadrupeds. Those of my own Institute are now proposing some experiments, which can be of very useful application to medicine, on the action of poisons and of drugs, especially of those which are called medicinal and heroic.

To do these experiments I have already made suitable arrangements with Signor Volta; and so, after having conferred with him about it, I have already performed a trial of experiments directed to determine the action of opium, of camphor, of musk, of snake-venom, of cherry laurel, of bitter almond, and others, with regard to exalting and abating animal electricity, applying these materials now to nerves and now to muscles, now in substance, and now by means of infusion, holding the animal for some time immersed, either intact or deprived of some parts. Within a short time I shall perhaps be in position to communicate to you the principal results of these, my researches.

We purpose still to investigate what may be the electric action of nerves on other parts than the muscles, that is on membranes and on vessels; and in what manner it modifies the circulation of fluids, the secretions, and other things; if indeed in this we have not been already forestalled by you, as supposes our most esteemed friend, Don Mariano Fontana, who esteems you as much as I, who do not allow myself to be surpassed by anyone in the honor of being, with the most distinguished consideration and greatest respect, yours.

Pavia.   3 April, 1792.

Letter from Doctor Luigi Galvani to
Professor Don Bassano Carminati

I have finally written out, in some manner, amid the scarcity of time in which I live daily, the few considerations pertaining to the experiments of the illustrious Signor Volta which I promised you in my latest. I beg you to submit them to the sagacious discernment of so illustrious a philosopher, to whom I entrust them and on whose judgment will depend principally their fate. They are expressed roughly and in confusion; in such a manner, that is, as the brevity of time and my scanty ability have permitted. But whereas he believed them not entirely useless, you can embellish them with the elegance of your style; therefore I consecrate them wholly to you.

The learned author, then, as you advise me, has measured the quantity of artificial electricity which, in a frog prepared and armatured in the manner proposed by me, suffices to produce muscular contractions, and has found this to be the tenth part of a degree of what is necessary to render it sensible to the most delicate electrometer, and thence he draws two beautiful conclusions: one is that the frog prepared in a similar way is an electrometer ten times more sensitive and delicate than any yet invented, and even than his own most delicate ones; the other is that a similar minute quantity of animal electricity will suffice to produce natural and spontaneous movements in the aforesaid animal; thence there comes by legitimate deduction the prodigious force which extrinsic electricity must have, whether it be terrestrial or atmospheric, in animals and thence in man, and therefore he had not yet sufficiently learned what and how great changes occurred to infer this either in one or in the other.

In short, in a very brief time he has shed no little light on the most interesting point of the influence of terrestrial and atmospheric electricity on our actions, and on the alterations and diseases which frequently afflict us; and in other animals he has no little encouraged the doctors to continue the use of artificial electricity, making them hope, with every reason, no small advantage.

He has made other beautiful experiments concerning the seat of the excess and of the deficiency of this animal electricity, referred to muscles and to nerves.

He has applied to the animal a Leyden jar charged on the internal surface, first in such a way that the hook corresponded to the nerves and the external surface to the muscles; then the opposite, and that in order to apply electricity from them according to my opinion, homologous in the first case, contrary in the second, I having suspected that the external part or surface of the muscular fibre is negatively electric and the internal positively, of which the nerve is like the conductor, invested with insulating material, to hinder the too easy and harmful dissipation of the electricity.

He having therefore observed that in the first case, when, that is, the hook is applied to the nerve, the contractions occurred, and not otherwise when the aforesaid hook is applied to the muscles, he began to suspect that the excess of that animal electricity is on the external surface of that muscle, the deficiency in its internal substance, to which the nerve corresponds, otherwise they would have been produced from homologous electricity, which is contrary to the established laws of physics concerning the same electricity.

Such just reasoning, founded on physical laws, and deduced from experiments by so accurate an experimentor and excellent a philosopher, you see well cannot but deserve my true approbation and the prompt change of my opinion, I certainly having no other goal in my researches than the pure and simple truth, with which alone can be joined that utility which I desire that some day these my researches and conjectures, such as they are, may bring.

I will beg you only to submit to the consideration of the learned philosopher this my doubt, I know not how important: that is, whether the contractions produced in case of applying the hook of the flask to the nerve could have been derived either totally or in part from the irruption into the same nerve, and thence into the internal surface of those muscle fibres, from the irruption, I said, of the electric fluid of the jar itself used in the experiment? For although in my hypothesis there ought to be two electric currents, that is the animal, or that of the internal surface of the muscular fibres, to which the nerve-conductor corresponds, and the artificial, that is, that of the hook, and although, I said, there ought to be between them these homologous electricities, yet it will be perhaps difficult that they should have been equal in every thing, both in quantity and in strength; but it will seem also sufficiently likely that the artificial current of the jar, though very slight, should have overcome the natural electricity of the nerve, that is, that of the internal surface of the muscular fibres. Thence a part of the electricity of the hook will have had to pass through the conducting substance of the nerve to the internal surface of the muscle fibres to render this electric on an equality with the internal surface of the jar, and therefore the effect, that is, the contraction, will have been a product not so much of the electricity existing in my sense within the internal part of the muscular fibres as it is much more of that of the jar added to it, mediating the application of the hook to the nerve.

If the courteous Signor Volta agrees with me in this, it would not prove difficult to explain the lack or smallness of the aforesaid contractions on applying the hook to the muscles, be it either to the external surface of the muscle or, I would say, of the animal phial: since, in such a state of things, the artificial electricity applied to the aforesaid external surface will surely have determined the exit of the animal electricity contained on the internal surface of this phial, but will not have been able to join it. This supposed animal electricity, as seems likely, in its quantity and energy being no little inferior to the artificial, considering singularly the dissipation of it which it seems must occur necessarily and continuously in the cutting and preparation of the animal, it will not cause surprise if it has not been sufficient to produce the sensible effect, which the artificial produced, or has not been able to produce it, except very slight and far inferior.

From which it results, I believe, that if the artificial electricity increases and this is applied equally to the muscles of the prepared frog, then determining it by the laws of the charge and discharge from the surfaces, there will go out from the muscle through the nerve a greater amount of natural electricity and with greater force; this is then sufficient to excite the contractions, or be they muscular motions, as I have proved many times by experiment; having constantly observed that a quantity of artificial electricity almost minimal suffices to induce contractions when it is applied to the nerve; it does not suffice when it is applied to the muscle. Therefore it would seem that, notwithstanding the beautiful experiments undertaken by the illustrious Signor Volta, to the contrary, the hypothesis could prevail of excess in the internal parts and surfaces of the muscle fibre, of deficiency in the external.

But even though the most illustrious Signor Volta should be willing courteously to grant me this, I shall not therefore remember his experiments without great appreciation for their great utility; while the same could conduce, assuming the aforesaid conjecture of the animal flask, to the clarification of a most interesting point of physiology, what is the physical cause of voluntary motions? and of one of the most difficult phenomena to understand in whatever system thus far invented concerning muscular motion. In fact his experiments will clearly demonstrate that the electric fluid can have muscular motions directly not only from the muscle to the nerve but starting from the nerve to the muscle, or be it from the brain to the muscle, and can occur not only through the means of the discharge, but again by means of a forced and impetuous overcharge of the supposed muscular phial: this being admitted, who does not see how happily successful is the explanation of voluntary muscular motions?

To excite these, the mind needs only, from the brain where it resides, with its marvellous and incomprehensible power and command to determine a greater quantity of animal electric fluid, collected in the brain, through the nerve-conductor to the muscle, or else perhaps to give a greater impulse to that which naturally exists in that muscle; the contractions then will occur no otherwise than they did with the most illustrious Signor Volta, when he added to the animal electricity of the nerve a little bit of artificial electricity and in consequence increased the impulse and the action of that which was static on the internal surface of the muscular fibre, in a sort of inertia and of idle equilibrium. But when electricity attaches itself to a surface of a Leyden jar, it goes out from the opposite surface by the law of equalization and of equilibrium of the two surfaces, and as much goes out from one as attaches itself to the other; therefore, attracting the same in the supposed muscular phial, as much neuro-electric fluid as will run from the brain through the nerve to the internal part, or be it surface, of the muscle, so much of it will go out from the opposite surface, or be it external part, of the same, that it is already always irrigated with conducting fluids, suited to disperse it and carry it out of the body, and thence there will always be room for a new supply and charge; in my supposition, the nerve, so much more than being a conductor of the animal jar, invested with insulating material, will never give place naturally to spontaneous discharges, which sometimes follow through union with atmosphere in the artificial jar.

Admitting such a constant ingress and egress of the said neural fluid from the muscle by known and constant laws, who does not see quickly that it is easy to explain it, how constantly the aforesaid fluid runs to the muscle without any of it accumulating therein either in excess or in a way which should impede the addition of a new supply, either naturally flowing from the brain to the same muscle, or determined there by the mind, a phenomenon which certainly in none of the systems hitherto invented is easily understood.

The experiments of such illustrious professors, and the easy explanation of such difficult phenomena, induce me for certain very willingly to change my opinion concerning the action of the mind on nerves, and the direction of the animal electric fluid in voluntary motions; the more, because some experiments tried by me a little while ago seem to confirm this same direction from the nerve to the internal surface of the muscle, and the demonstration seems not less suitable than the opposite to excite muscular motions.

I have presented, as I mention in my little work, the feet of the prepared frog to the external surface of a Leyden jar charged internally, and have observed that the contractions occur at the extraction of the spark. I have then, moreover, in a dark place at the external surface of the same jar, likewise reversed the external surface of another small jar similarly charged, out from which sprang the conductor with its point bent in the opposite direction to the aforesaid surface, and I have seen that at the extraction of the spark from the former, the luminous tuft of the conductor of the latter went out instead of reviving, as follows when the aforesaid conductor is reversed at the external surface of the jar indicated.

Such disappearance of the luminous tuft demonstrates that, in the act of extraction of the spark from this jar, the electricity of the other is forced into a retrograde motion and to direct itself no longer from the cavity to the conductor, as it did when the vanished tuft reappeared at the extraction of the spark, but certainly with the opposite direction, that is, from the conductor to the cavity of the same flask. It would have taken this opposite direction more easily and more promptly, if there had been near the point of the aforesaid conductor such a conducting body as communicated with the ground; while then the electricity of the earth, determined by the same law of equilibrium of the surfaces to the internal surface of the same flask, entered through the aforesaid conductor to betake itself to the same surface. The same thing, it seems, must also happen to the electricity of the animal flask, whence occur the contractions when its external surface reverses itself, or be it the feet at the external surface of the flask, from which the spark is extracted, and they are greater and stronger if there is near its conductor or the nerve, in the act of extracting the spark, a body similarly communicating with the earth.

It seems that the same ought to occur if the air contiguous to the aforesaid conductor contains much electricity, or else if there be nearby some body which can supply some. Thence perhaps are obtained sometimes the aforesaid contractions, if there is near the feet of the animal a cylinder of powdered sulphur, and they are also and at such times greater if there is applied simultaneously to the exposed spinal cord a glass cylinder similarly excited, although they do not occur with the sole application of that glass cylinder although well rubbed; since by means of the negative electricity of the sulphur the electricity flowing from the spinal cord is compelled to return to the internal surface of the muscle from which it departed; and the electricity is determined, be it by the air or by the glass, to make its way into the spinal cord, and thence much more to compel the retrograde motion of that animal electricity.

Whence it results that the same being repelled by two forces towards the said internal surface, the effect is too great, and thence arise those contractions which we said are stronger; which afterwards fail on the application of the activated glass alone to the spinal cord, perhaps because, dealing with homologous electricity, there can enter into the spinal cord only that small portion of vitreous electricity, which overcomes the animal electricity, and that with difficulty, remaining by nature strongly adherent to the glass. Thence it is that in case of employing sulphur and activated glass, to make the aforesaid contractions much more perceptible, in the manner described, it helps a great deal, before trying the experiment, to armature both the spinal cord and the muscles with tinfoil, and to apply to them any metallic conductor; on the contrary, so great is the strength of this armature that then the contractions are obtained by applying to the aforesaid muscle conductor the powdered sulphur alone, and that very likely because the discharge from the external surface of the muscles takes place more easily, and because of a prompter return of the animal electricity to the internal surface of the muscle through the nerve, and an easier introduction into it of whatever electricity is found in the contiguous air.

From the outcome and result here expounded, if I do not explain and express myself ill, it is clearly understood that muscular contractions can be produced by natural electricity in the living animal from three different causes: first from a violent overcharge of the muscular cell induced by the powers of the mind, and this seems to occur in voluntary motions; second from a forced overcharge, as when, by some external agent or irritation, the aforesaid electricity is determined to descend forcibly and violently from the brain to the muscles, as in reflex motions, and I call this action an overcharge, assuming that some charge, as seems very likely, is in the muscle constantly and naturally; third and finally from a charge equally violent and forced, as will occur when some external agent, applied to the nerve or to the brain, determines the electricity of the internal surface of the muscle to ascend through the nerve and go back to the external surface of that muscle.

Given these three causes, it seemed to me that I saw open a wide field for the felicitous explanation, not only of voluntary motions, but also of unnatural and violent ones; and of various nervous maladies and their causes, as also of their relations to terrestrial and atmospheric electricity, as I shall endeavor to demonstrate in another little book of mine which I shall publish as soon as possible, when pressing occupations do not forbid me.

Therefore, before adopting the explanation and the theory of the overcharge principally in voluntary motions, I desire that you and the illustrious professor should judge if ever he could render it subject to any question that it is founded on principles less certain than those on which is based the theory of the charge, and that it needs more suppositions than the other; while I recognize the aforesaid opinion as founded on the action of an extrinsic and artificial electricity, whereas this is based on the action of an electricity purely intrinsic and natural, it is proper and reasonable to suppose, in the former, that the artificial electricity acts on the nerve in the same manner as the natural, but is not wholly the same; for although it appears very similar, yet it is not demonstrated, but there remains room for suspicion that the artificial electricity acts in the manner of a stimulus and determines the natural to discharge; and it seems likely, whatever difference of nature there happens to be between them, through some mutation, or I would say preparation and modification, that the aforesaid common electricity derives from the animal machine; whereas in the hypothesis of the discharge there is no need of any such supposition, but it is sufficient to assume that, as natural electricity acts in animals dead and artificially prepared, so it acts in the living; a supposition which, although it is certainly daring, is nevertheless, as everyone sees, common to both hypotheses.

Moreover the phenomenon of the perennial influx of neuro-electric fluid from the brain to the muscle through the nerve, without either the muscle or the nerve remaining full of it to excess, and without access ever being denied to a new quantity of the same fluid coming up, it is easy to understand that in a state of quiet of the muscle it is explained with equal felicity whether on one or on the other hypothesis, because the felicity of such explanation springs from the supposed structure of the muscular fibre like a Leyden phial, which is equally common to one and the other conjecture. Moreover, in a state of motion of the same muscle, where this succeeds in the discharge of the muscle fibre, it would certainly not impede a new afflux of the aforesaid neuro-electric fluid to the muscle, but would render it much more active and abundant, the supposed muscle cell finding itself, after the motion, charged either wholly or in part.

These reflections, whatever may be their value, render me at present undecided to which of the two hypotheses the preference ought to be given, until your judgment and that of the distinguished author and of your other illustrious colleagues have determined me more to one than to the other, to which sagacious judgment I submit both these and all the other reflections hitherto communicated to you, and on that my opinion and conjecture will always depend—somewhat.

This morning in our Hospital of Saint Ursula, in which the Professor of Surgery is the learned and my most distinguished colleague Doctor Gaspar Gentili, excellent master of surgery, I tested, with my customary devices, an amputated leg and arm, immediately after the operation, in the presence of the aforesaid professor and other physicians and men of learning, and the flexor muscles of the thumb and of the adjacent digits were seen to contract, both of the hand and of the foot, and in consequence the aforesaid digits to move.

The device which I employed was to place a good part of the leg and of the foot, denuded of their integuments, immediately in warm water, and then to armature the corresponding nerves of the indicated muscles with tin-foil close to their entrance into the same; then I applied a little conducting metal cap, and singularly of silver, and I applied it in such a way that with one part it touched the edge of the tin-foil, and with another the portion of nerve uncovered or some contiguous part, so that there was, as I suppose, an arc composed partly of the aforesaid metals, partly of extrinsic moisture, which brought back to the external surface of the indicated muscles the natural electricity of the internal surface, which had ascended to the place of contact of the nerve, and from that had gone out through the force of the same contact.

The same nerves were then invested with wax or with some other insulating body, or else the same bodies were superimposed on the first armature, and no further contraction then was obtained. Therefore the existence of animal electricity seems proved, and its law in man also proposed. But I do not wish to detain you with it at greater length. You will perhaps have been too much annoyed with the excessive number of things described here and with the prolixity of the test, but pardon all to the pleasure which I have of conferring with you, and to my desire of receiving from you those enlightenments which from your courtesy and erudition I cannot promise myself too abundantly. With the truest esteem.

Bologna.   8 May, 1792.